CREATION MUSEUM

SIGNS

First printing: January 2021

Master Books® is a division of the New Leaf Publishing Group, Inc.

ISBN: 978-1-68344-179-3
ISBN: 978-1-61458-773-6 (digital)

Library of Congress Number: 2020950780
Cover by Diana Bogardus

Please consider requesting that a copy of this volume be purchased by your local library system.

Printed in the United States

Please visit our website for other great titles:
www.masterbooks.com

For information regarding author interviews, please contact the publicity department at (870) 438-5288.

Master Books®
A Division of New Leaf Publishing Group
www.masterbooks.com

Creation Museum, Petersburg, KY

Introduction

I have been blessed with the opportunity to develop the signage content for many of the exhibits at the Creation Museum. From a personal perspective, it is exciting to walk through a finished exhibit knowing that I played a key role in what people see, and it is gratifying to know that my words can be read by hundreds of thousands of people every year. But far more important than any personal satisfaction is the reality that these signs teach the biblical worldview, defend the Scriptures, and proclaim the gospel of Jesus Christ.

Another benefit of my role is that I regularly consult with specialists on the topics addressed in the exhibits. My areas of expertise relate to biblical studies, theology, and church history, and my assistant, Mike Belknap, specializes in animal studies, so it is extremely helpful for us to be able to discuss other subjects with experts in relevant disciplines. For example, while researching the Fearfully & Wonderfully Made exhibit, we consulted Dr. David Menton (biology and anatomy), Dr. Georgia Purdom (molecular genetics), and Dr. Elizabeth Mitchell (obstetrics and gynecology) in their areas of expertise.

Working with talented designers, artists, and fabricators is another blessing of my position. Each exhibit is the result of countless hours of brainstorming, planning, research, design, and construction. The exhibit designers shape the room's theme and design in a way that points people to the teaching and reinforces it. Then the talented graphic designers take the content and create the eye-catching signs guests encounter in the museum.

There are several interesting challenges presented by each exhibit. For example, how should the teaching be arranged to help people understand it? How much information can go on each sign? How can we state something in a way appropriate for a non-denominational ministry?

Finally, since our exhibits focus on teaching biblical history and doctrine, we have a serious responsibility to make sure God's Word is handled faithfully. Thus, every word is carefully examined in light of Scripture and undergoes a thorough review process.

We trust you will find these signs to be informative and God-honoring as we point people to our Creator and Savior, Jesus Christ.

Sincerely,
Tim Chaffey,
Content Manager, Attractions Division of Answers in Genesis

A special recognition goes to Mike Matthews who served as content manager when the Creation Museum opened. Approximately half of the signs in this book were written by him.

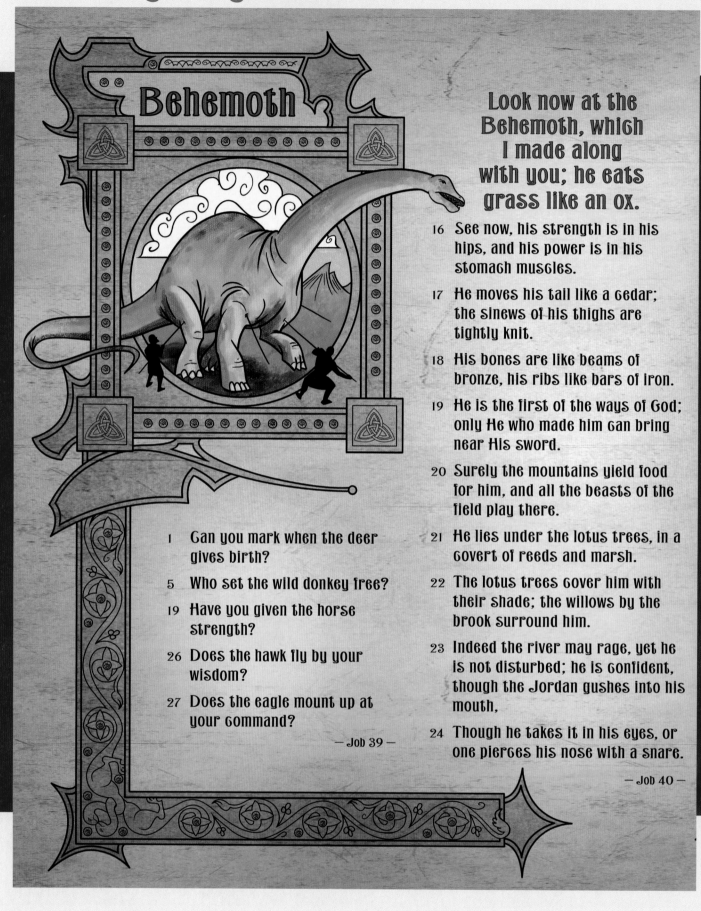

Behemoth

Look now at the Behemoth, which I made along with you; he eats grass like an ox.

16 See now, his strength is in his hips, and his power is in his stomach muscles.

17 He moves his tail like a cedar; the sinews of his thighs are tightly knit.

18 His bones are like beams of bronze, his ribs like bars of iron.

19 He is the first of the ways of God; only He who made him can bring near His sword.

20 Surely the mountains yield food for him, and all the beasts of the field play there.

21 He lies under the lotus trees, in a covert of reeds and marsh.

22 The lotus trees cover him with their shade; the willows by the brook surround him.

23 Indeed the river may rage, yet he is not disturbed; he is confident, though the Jordan gushes into his mouth,

24 Though he takes it in his eyes, or one pierces his nose with a snare.

— Job 40 —

1 Can you mark when the deer gives birth?

5 Who set the wild donkey free?

19 Have you given the horse strength?

26 Does the hawk fly by your wisdom?

27 Does the eagle mount up at your command?

— Job 39 —

 an you draw out Leviathan with a hook, or snare his tongue with a line which you lower?

2 Can you put a reed through his nose, or pierce his jaw with a hook?

9 Indeed, any hope of overcoming him is false; shall one not be overwhelmed at the sight of him?

18 His sneezings flash forth light, and his eyes are like the eyelids of the morning.

19 Out of his mouth go burning lights; sparks of fire shoot out.

20 Smoke goes out of his nostrils, as from a boiling pot and burning rushes.

21 His breath kindles coals, and a flame goes out of his mouth.

22 Strength dwells in his neck, and sorrow dances before him.

23 The folds of his flesh are joined together; they are firm on him and cannot be moved.

24 His heart is as hard as stone, even as hard as the lower millstone.

25 When he raises himself up, the mighty are afraid; because of his crashings they are beside themselves.

26 Though the sword reaches him, it cannot avail; nor does spear, dart, or javelin.

27 He regards iron as straw, and bronze as rotten wood.

28 The arrow cannot make him flee; slingstones become like stubble to him.

— Job 41 —

Leviathan

Not the Stuff of Legends!

The Bible is authoritative, without error, and inspired by God

While dragon legends may be fanciful retellings of actual events
God's Word tells us about two real dragon-like creatures

Were Dinosaurs Dragons?

Some dragons flew and other dragons lived in the water, so not all dragons could be called dinosaurs. But all dinosaurs could have been dragons.

Some reptiles are mistakenly called dinosaurs.

Dinosaur

Legs directly under the body
Land-dwelling animal

Not a Dinosaur

Dimetrodon (legs out to the side)
Plesiosaurs (marine reptiles)
Pterosaurs (flying reptiles)

Dragon Legends: Fact or Fiction?

Legends of an ancient flood exist in hundreds of cultures around the world. A large number of these traditions share common elements with the biblical Flood described in Genesis. For example, many of these stories assert that man's wickedness brought divine judgment upon the whole world and that eight people and some animals survived aboard a large boat.

The Bible provides the historical account of the worldwide Flood. By carefully comparing these legends with God's Word, we see that many of these traditions have distorted, embellished, or lost information about the actual events.

Similarly, cultures from all over the globe also have dragon legends. Epic battles between gallant knights and fierce dragons are rather common, and the descriptions of these beasts are often very similar to those of dinosaurs.

Of course, ancient people would not have called them "dinosaurs," since that word was coined in 1841. Carvings and cave paintings of these monsters have been discovered. Some of these dragon legends contain mythical elements, while others likely lost all the true details and retain nothing more than tall tales. But in many cases, the dragons were viewed as real animals. Do some of these dragon legends actually speak of dinosaurs?

In the Bible, God told Job about two creatures that could be considered dragons: the Behemoth and the Leviathan. Some Christians suggest that these are mythical monsters, but the mention of Behemoth and Leviathan in the book of Job follows the descriptions of about a dozen real animals. Furthermore, why would God tell Job to consider two beasts that did not even exist?

DRAGON LEGENDS
AROUND THE WORLD

Ogopogo · Champ · Thunderbird · Quetzalcoatl · Apatosaurus Pictograph · Nessie · Beowulf · St. George and the Dragon · Hydra · Mokele-mbembe · Kongamato · Ishtar Gate · Chinese Dragon · Ta Prohm Petroglyph · Burrunjor · Ropen

Eighth-century scholar John of Damascus wrote *On Dragons and Ghosts*, in which he differentiated between real creatures and fictional creatures. After describing some dragons as extremely large serpents, he stated:

There is one more kind of [dragon]; those [that] have wide head, goldish eyes and horny protuberances on the back of the head. They also have a beard [protruding] out of the throat ... This dragon is a sort of [beast], like the rest of the animals, for it has a beard, like a goat, and horn at the back of its head. Its eyes are big and goldish. These dragons can be both big and small. All serpent kinds are poisonous, except dragons, for they do not emit poison.

Famed thirteenth-century explorer Marco Polo described dragons in the Far East:

In this province [Carajan] are found snakes and great serpents of such vast size as to strike fear into those who see them ... Some of them are ten paces in length ... The bigger ones are about ten palms in girth. They have two forelegs near the head, but for foot nothing but a claw.... The head is very big, and the eyes are bigger than a great loaf of bread. The mouth is large enough to swallow a man whole, and is garnished with great [pointed] teeth.

The animals described here are believable, and these men intended to relay information about what they had discovered. Did these men actually see or hear about real dragons—creatures that are today called dinosaurs?

ST. GEORGE
and the Dragon

St. George (c. AD 275–303) was a devout Christian and Roman military officer. The famous legend of his battle with the dragon is said to have occurred during his journey to join his men in Diocletian's army.

As he neared the city of Selene in Libya, he saw a young princess outside the city wall. She pleaded with him to leave so that he would not be killed by the dragon to which she was being offered as a sacrifice. George refused to leave and vowed to protect her.

Suddenly, the dragon appeared and attacked the soldier. During his fierce battle against the fire-breathing foe, George found a weak spot under the beast's left wing and delivered a crippling blow. The legend explains that the princess then led the maimed creature back into the city, where George killed it in the presence of the people.

The king asked George what he wanted as a reward. The dragonslayer replied, "I desire only that ye believe in the God who strengthened my hand to gain this victory." After baptizing the city into the Christian faith, George resumed his trek to join his troops.

BEOWULF and the Dragon

Originally written in Old English, the epic poem Beowulf is named for its hero and tells of his mighty deeds in sixth-century Scandinavia, a time known as the Vendel Era.

The most famous creature in the tale is Grendel, a fierce monster that devoured scores of Danish nobles. Beowulf defeated this creature by ripping its arm from the socket, causing the beast to bleed to death. The hero also defeated Grendel's mother, as well as numerous sea dragons.

Beowulf died from wounds sustained from a vicious fire dragon that terrorized the land after a thief had stolen a golden cup from the beast's hoard. Aided by a brave warrior, Beowulf vanquished the flying dragon and saved the land.

The epic contains accurate historical information as well as fiction. The stories of battling dragons may be legendary, but do they have any basis in reality? Did these men or their ancestors actually fight dinosaurs and pterosaurs? This idea would be consistent with the Bible. But those who believe dinosaurs lived millions of years before man cannot adequately explain why cultures around the world have dragon legends whose creatures often match descriptions of dinosaurs.

DRAGON LEGENDS
AROUND THE WORLD

Red Dragon of Wales

Many tales describe how Y Ddraig Goch ("the red dragon") came to be closely associated with Wales. One popular story tells of an epic battle between a red dragon and a white dragon in which the red dragon saved the people of the land by defeating the white dragon.

the Lernaean Hydra

According to Greek mythology, Hercules performed twelve labors, including a battle with a great creature known as the Hydra. This serpentine dragon had nine heads and poisonous breath. When one head was cut off, two more would grow in its place. Hercules battled fiercely and ultimately defeated the serpent.

Quetzalcoatl

The Mesoamerican Aztecs and Toltecs worshipped the feathered serpent Quetzalcoatl (called Kukulcan by the Maya people). According to their mythology, he was the god of the wind and the morning and evening stars.

Daniel and the Dragon

Not accepted as part of the Old Testament canon by Jews or Protestants, the Apocrypha include extra chapters in the book of Daniel. Here we are told about Daniel's encounter with a great dragon.

The king of Babylon commanded Daniel to worship his dragon as a god. The prophet refused and told the king that he could prove the creature was not a god by killing it without sword or club. Daniel made cakes of pitch, fat, and hair and fed them to the dragon, causing it to burst open.

Athanasius Kircher (1601-1680) has been called a polymath (a person with encyclopedic learning). In his exhaustive study of everything underground, *Mundus Subterraneus*, Kircher included a chapter on dragons, describing multiple dragon artifacts and legendary encounters with the beasts. He covered the dragon like any other animal in his book, citing their dwellings (often caves) and habits:

Of winged dragons, dispute has only arisen between authors, most of whom declare them to be fanciful, but these authors are contradicted by the histories and eyewitnesses. Winged dragons—small, great, and greatest—have been produced in all times in every land.

Known as the "father of history," Herodotus (fifth century BC) was a Greek historian who traveled extensively and reported what he heard and saw. He described a boneyard in Arabia filled with skeletons of winged serpents and explained where they came from:

Winged serpents are said to fly from Arabia at the beginning of spring, making for Egypt; but the ibis birds encounter the invaders in this pass and kill them ... The serpents are like water snakes. Their wings are not feathered but very like the wings of a bat.

Both of these men wrote more about dragons and flying serpents. Could they possibly have been writing about creatures we call pterosaurs?

STARTING POINTS

EXPLORE TWO VIEWS OF THE SAME EVIDENCE

NATURALISTIC
EVOLUTION

BIBLICAL
CREATION

SAME ROCKS. FOSSILS. PLANTS. PEOPLE. ANIMALS. OCEANS. CONTINENTS. WORLD. STARS. UNIVERSE. EVIDENCE

WHY DO CREATIONISTS AND EVOLUTIONISTS REACH DIFFERENT CONCLUSIONS?

DID DINOSAURS AND HUMANS COEXIST?

NATURALISTIC
EVOLUTIONIST
WORLDVIEW

▸ In recent years, birds have been reclassified as avian dinosaurs, but humans have never lived at the same time as non-avian dinosaurs.

"Non-bird dinosaurs lived between about 245 and 66 million years ago, in a time known as the Mesozoic Era. This was many millions of years before the first modern humans, Homo sapiens, appeared."
—The Natural History Museum[1]

"We keep dinosaurs as pets, eat them, enjoy looking at them in nature and in zoos, and treat them as mascots for some of our favorite sports teams."
—Stephen Brusatte[2]

[1] "When Did Dinosaurs Live?" at www.nhm.ac.uk/discover/when-did-dinosaurs-live.html

[2] John Pickrell, "Could Humans and Dinosaurs Coexist? Here's the Science" at www.nationalgeographic.com/news/2018/06/dinosaurs-humans-coexist-jurassic-world-paleontology-science

BIBLICAL
CREATIONIST
WORLDVIEW

▸ Dinosaurs and all other land animals were created on the sixth day—the same day as the first man and woman and one day after the flying creatures (Genesis 1:20–31). Thus, dinosaurs lived at the same time as man and did not evolve into birds.

"And God made the beasts of the earth according to their kinds, the livestock according to their kinds, and all the creatures that creep along the ground according to their kinds...Then God said, 'Let us make man in our image, after our likeness.'
And there was evening, and there was morning, the sixth day."—Genesis 1:25–26, 31

WAS THERE A
GLOBAL FLOOD?

NATURALISTIC
EVOLUTIONIST
WORLDVIEW

▸ At no point in earth's history was it ever completely covered by water.

"There simply is no good evidence that a global flood ever happened...The story of Noah is self-contradictory, uncorroborated by independent historical evidence, and is generally at odds with everything we know about our planet's geology, biology, and species diversity." —Kyle Hill[1]

BIBLICAL
CREATIONIST
WORLDVIEW

▸ The Bible unequivocally teaches that the Genesis Flood destroyed the whole world and all the land animals that were not aboard Noah's Ark.

"And the waters increased greatly on the earth and covered all the high hills under the whole heaven. The waters prevailed above the mountains, covering them fifteen cubits deep. And all creatures that moved on the earth died—birds, cattle, beasts, all the creatures that swarm on the earth, and all mankind." —Genesis 7:19–21

[1] Kyle Hill, "Noah Isn't Accurate Because It Can't Be" at blogs.discovermagazine.com/but-not-simpler/2014/03/28/noah-isnt-accurate-cant

ARE HUMAN "RACES" EQUAL?

NATURALISTIC
EVOLUTIONIST
WORLDVIEW

▶ While most evolutionists reject racism, their philosophy is inherently racist.

"Biological arguments for racism may have been common before 1850, but they increased by orders of magnitude following the acceptance of evolutionary theory. The litany is familiar: cold, dispassionate, objective, modern science shows us that races can be ranked on a scale of superiority. If this offends Christian morality or a sentimental belief in human unity, so be it; science must be free to proclaim unpleasant truths."
—Stephen Jay Gould[1]

BIBLICAL
CREATIONIST
WORLDVIEW

▶ All human beings are made in God's image and are descendants of Adam, so there is no basis for racism from a biblical perspective.

"And He has made from one man every nation of men to dwell on the face of all the earth"—Acts 17:26

"And Adam called his wife's name Eve, because she was the mother of all the living"—Genesis 3:20

[1] Stephen Jay Gould, *Ontogeny and Phylogeny* (Cambridge, MA: The Belknap Press of Harvard University Press, 1977), p. 127.

ARE HUMANS AND APES RELATED?

NATURALISTIC
EVOLUTIONIST
WORLDVIEW

▸ Humans and apes share a common ancestor that lived several million years ago.

"The human lineage diverged from that of apes at least seven million years ago and maybe as long as 13 million years ago. The earliest undisputed members of our lineage to regularly walk upright were the australopithecines, of which the most famous is Lucy's species, Australopithecus afarensis. (Lucy herself is dated to 3.2 million years ago.)"
—Human Evolution 101[1]

BIBLICAL
CREATIONIST
WORLDVIEW

▸ God created the land animals, including the apes, on the Sixth Day. Then He made man in His image from the dust of the ground—not from an ape-like ancestor.

Then God said, "Let us make man in our image, after our likeness. Let them rule over the fish of the sea, the birds of the air, and every creature that moves on the ground."—Genesis 1:26

The LORD God formed man from the dust of the ground and breathed into his nostrils the breath of life, and the man became a living being.—Genesis 2:7

[1] Nadia Drake, "Human Evolution 101" at www.nationalgeographic.com/news/2015/09/human-evolution-101

WHO IS JESUS?

NATURALISTIC
EVOLUTIONIST
WORLDVIEW

▸ Most atheists believe Jesus of Nazareth was a real person, but they reject His deity and miracles. A vocal minority of modern atheists deny that Jesus even existed.

"The consensus of scholars, including non-Christian scholars, is that a historical Jesus most likely existed and the later stories about 'Jesus Christ' were told about him. The idea that there was no such historical person at all and that 'Jesus Christ' was a purely mythical figure has been posited in one form or another since the eighteenth century, but is not taken seriously by anyone but a tiny handful of fringe scholars and amateurs."—Tim O'Neill[1]

[1] Tim O'Neill, "Did Jesus Exist? The Jesus Myth Theory, Again" at historyforatheists.com/2017/05/did-jesus-exist-the-jesus-myth-theory-again

BIBLICAL
CREATIONIST
WORLDVIEW

▸ Jesus is the Son of God—our Creator, Savior, and Lord.

"In the beginning was the Word, and the Word was with God, and the Word was God...And the Word became flesh and dwelt among us."—John 1:1, 14

"He is the image of the invisible God, the firstborn over all creation. He created all things that are in heaven and that are on earth, visible and invisible, whether thrones or dominions or principalities or powers. All things were created through Him and for Him. He is before all things, and in Him all things hold together."—Colossians 1:15–17

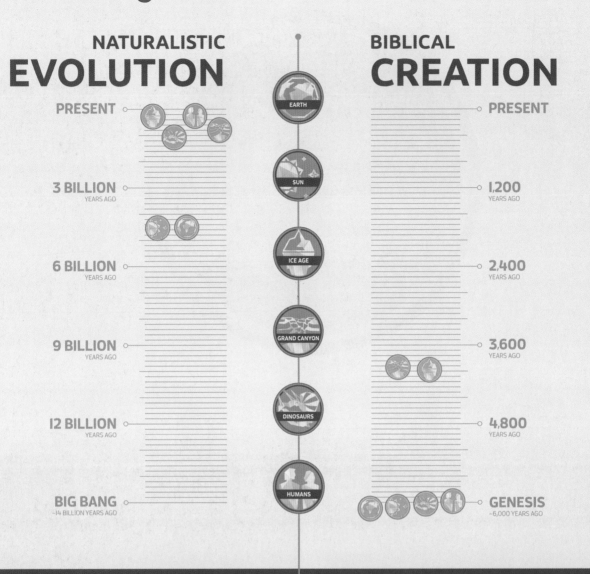

NATURALISTIC
EVOLUTION

BIBLICAL
CREATION

PRESENT	EARTH	PRESENT
3 BILLION YEARS AGO	SUN	1,200 YEARS AGO
6 BILLION YEARS AGO	ICE AGE	2,400 YEARS AGO
9 BILLION YEARS AGO	GRAND CANYON	3,600 YEARS AGO
12 BILLION YEARS AGO	DINOSAURS	4,800 YEARS AGO
BIG BANG ~14 BILLION YEARS AGO	HUMANS	GENESIS ~6,000 YEARS AGO

TWO MODELS

Creationists and evolutionists share the same data. We study the same fossils, trees, and stars. We observe the same world, but we reach different conclusions because we have different starting points. Each worldview develops its own models to explain the data. Consider how these two models understand six sets of data.

EARTH   SUN   ICE AGE   GRAND CANYON   DINOSAURS   HUMANS

CHANGING **EVOLUTIONIST** MODELS

Evolutionary models are frequently adjusted based on new findings and updated understandings of existing data. Occasionally, outdated models are discarded and replaced by new models.

LAMARCKISM

In the early 1800s, French biologist Jean Baptiste Lamarck popularized an early evolutionary idea to explain how animals gradually acquired certain traits. He thought that an animal might pass on characteristics it had gained during its lifetime. The classic example is the giraffe's long neck. Lamarck believed that giraffes originally had shorter necks, but if one continually stretched upward for foliage, it might develop a slightly longer neck, and that acquired characteristic would be passed on to the next generation. Lamarckism was replaced by Darwinism, which posits natural selection as the mechanism that drove the evolution of the giraffe's neck.

CHANGING **CREATIONIST** MODELS

Creationists build scientific models, interpreting the evidence as they understand it in light of Scripture. Although the models based on the Bible can be modified, refined, and even discarded, the Bible itself does not change.

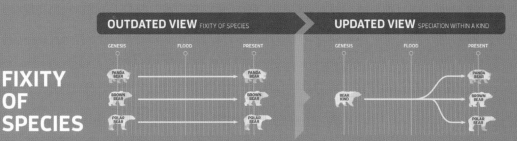

OUTDATED VIEW FIXITY OF SPECIES

UPDATED VIEW SPECIATION WITHIN A KIND

GENESIS FLOOD PRESENT

PANDA BEAR
BROWN BEAR
POLAR BEAR

BEAR KIND

PANDA BEAR
BROWN BEAR
POLAR BEAR

FIXITY OF SPECIES

In the 1800s, some Christians believed that God created each of the species in their respective forms and locations. They did not realize that new species can develop quickly due to the incredible amount of genetic diversity God created within each kind of organism. This belief in the fixity of species provided an opportunity for Charles Darwin to popularize his evolutionary view, which is based on observable changes within types of animals. However, since no new traits are produced that could change one kind of animal into another kind, the changes we observe do not support evolution.

THE EVIDENCE EXISTS
IN THE PRESENT

NOT ALL SCIENCE IS THE SAME

OBSERVATIONAL SCIENCE

deals with *testing* and *verifying* ideas in the present. Chemistry experiments in a laboratory and the ongoing study of a medicine's effectiveness in treating a particular disease are examples of observational science.

HISTORICAL SCIENCE

involves the *interpretation* of evidence from the past that now exists in the present. A paleontologist's narrative of a fossilized creature's habits and an astronomer's explanation of a star's formation are examples of historical science.

RADIOMETRIC DATING

Does radiometric dating prove that most of earth's rock layers and fossils are much older than what a plain reading of Scripture teaches?

Are dates obtained by radiometric dating reliable, and are they more trustworthy than God's Word?

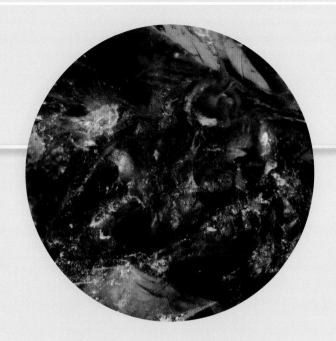

GEOLOGY

SAPPHIRES

OBSERVATIONAL
Where was the gemstone found?
What is it made of?

HISTORICAL
In most cases, it would be historical science to ask how and when the gemstone formed. However, this is an artificial sapphire, grown in three weeks by Crystal Systems in Salem, Massachusetts, so we know how and when it was formed.

ASTRONOMY

STARLIGHT

OBSERVATIONAL
What is the color, speed, and direction of the light?

HISTORICAL
How and when were the stars made?
How quickly did light travel to earth from distant stars?

- Some use the speed of light and extrapolate into the past for billions of years.
- Biblical creationists have developed models to explain how light from the stars reached the earth in a short timeframe.

> **Did you know?**
> Light years are a measure of distance, not time. Also, when astronomers study starlight they are not directly observing the past, as some have claimed. Rather, they are looking at the light in the present, after it has been affected by cosmic dust and gravity as it traveled through space.

PALEONTOLOGY

ARCHAEOPTERYX

OBSERVATIONAL
Where was the creature found?
How big was the animal?
What was its skeletal structure?

HISTORICAL
When did the animal live?
What was its diet?
How did it behave?
Which creatures was it related to?

This is a cast of an Archaeopteryx lithographica specimen from the Solnhofen Limestone (Jurassic System), Germany.

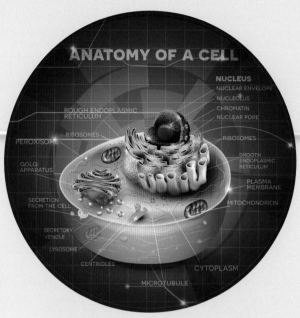

ANATOMY OF A CELL

NUCLEUS
NUCLEAR ENVELOPE
NUCLEOLUS
CHROMATIN
NUCLEAR PORE

ROUGH ENDOPLASMIC
RETICULUM

RIBOSOMES

RIBOSOMES

PEROXISOME

SMOOTH
ENDOPLASMIC
RETICULUM

GOLGI
APPARATUS

PLASMA
MEMBRANE

SECRETION
FROM THE CELL

MITOCHONDRION

SECRETORY
VESICLE

LYSOSOME

CENTRIOLES

CYTOPLASM

MICROTUBULE

BIOLOGY

CELL

OBSERVATIONAL
Every living cell displays amazing complexity, nullifying the outdated concept of a simple cell.

Each organelle within the cell has specific functions to perform.

HISTORICAL
Did this microscopic complexity arise by blind chance or was it designed by its Creator?

Did you know?
When Charles Darwin popularized the idea of evolution, it was generally believed that the cell was essentially a nucleus with its surrounding cytoplasm. We now know that cells are remarkably complex, containing our DNA and a number of intricate structures. They generate energy (ATP), import nutrients, secrete waste, and are capable of self-repair and self-replication.

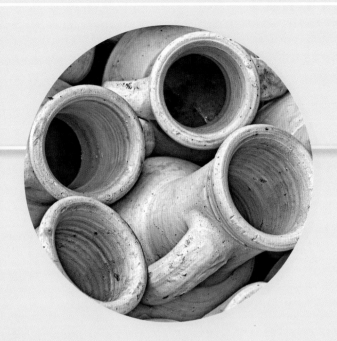

ARCHAEOLOGY

POTTERY

OBSERVATIONAL

Where was it found?

When was it made?

>It is generally safe to assume that the clay vessel was made before items found in soil above it and after those discovered beneath it.

HISTORICAL

Who made it and what was its purpose?

>These can often be determined with some confidence.

When was it made?

>Obtaining an absolute date for many ancient items relies upon multiple assumptions.

HOW IT IS SUPPOSED TO WORK

The atoms of certain elements occasionally become radioactive isotopes, meaning they become unstable when they have too many neutrons in their nuclei. Over time, the isotope ejects particles from its nucleus until it becomes stable.

The rate at which an isotope undergoes this decay process is known as its half-life. The half-life is the amount of time required for half of the unstable atoms to become stable atoms. Technically, the radioactive element does not decay, as though it disintegrates, but it transforms from the original or parent element into the new or daughter element, sometimes through many steps.

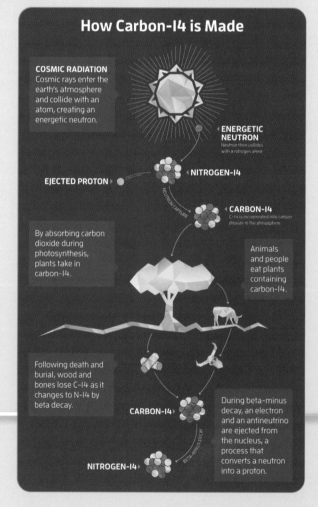

How Carbon-14 is Made

COSMIC RADIATION
Cosmic rays enter the earth's atmosphere and collide with an atom, creating an energetic neutron.

ENERGETIC NEUTRON
Neutron then collides with a nitrogen atom

EJECTED PROTON

NITROGEN-14

NEUTRON CAPTURE

CARBON-14
C-14 is incorporated into carbon dioxide in the atmosphere

By absorbing carbon dioxide during photosynthesis, plants take in carbon-14.

Animals and people eat plants containing carbon-14.

Following death and burial, wood and bones lose C-14 as it changes to N-14 by beta decay.

CARBON-14

During beta-minus decay, an electron and an antineutrino are ejected from the nucleus, a process that converts a neutron into a proton.

BETA-MINUS DECAY

NITROGEN-14

HALF-LIFE EXAMPLES

Radioactive Isotope (parent)	Stable (daughter)	Half-Life
Uranium-238	Lead-206	4.47 billion years
Potassium-40	Argon-40	1.25 billion years
Plutonium-239	Lead-207	24,000 years
Carbon-14	Nitrogen-14	5,730 years
Polonium-210	Lead-206	138 days
Technetium-99m	Technetium-99	6 hours

Many people have been taught that carbon dating proves the earth is billions of years old. However, carbon-14 dating is not used to calculate the earth's age. Even if it were, it never yields dates in the millions or billions of years because the half-life of carbon-14 is 5,730 years. Also, carbon-14 dating has a practical limit of 65,000–70,000 years. Isotopes with longer half-lives, such as uranium-238, are used to calculate dates in the billions of years.

PROBLEMS WITH RADIOMETRIC DATING

Numerous examples can be found when radiometric dating miserably fails to provide an accurate date when the age of the item is known.

Sample	Known Age	Radiometric Age (K-Ar)*
Mt. St. Helens rock [1]	**Formed 1986**	**300,000–400,000 years**
Mt. Etna basalt [2]	**Formed 1964**	**690,000–710,000 years**
Hawaii, Hualālai basalt [2]	**Formed 1800–1801**	**6,300,000–39,300,000 years**

In some cases, two adjacent items yield wildly divergent dates.

Wood buried in basalt [3] *(New Zealand, Mt. Rangitito)*	**Wood (C-14)***	**225 years**	*Wood and basalt should be the same age*
	Basalt (K-Ar)*	**465,000 years**	

Wood buried under basalt [4] *(Australia, Crinum-Emerald)*	**Wood (C-14)***	**37,500 years**	*Wood should be older or the same age as the basalt*
	Basalt (K-Ar)*	**36.7 million years**	

* C-14 refers to carbon-14 dating, and K-Ar refers to potassium-argon dating.
[1] Keith Swenson, "Radio-Dating in Rubble" at answersingenesis.org
[2] Andrew A. Snelling, "The Cause of Anomalous Potassium-Argon 'Ages' for Recent Andesite Flows at Mt. Ngauruhoe, New Zealand, and the Implications for Potassium-Argon 'Dating'" at answersingenesis.org
[3] Harold Coffin, *Origin by Design* (Hagerstown, MD: Review and Herald Publishing, 1983), p. 400
[4] Andrew A. Snelling, "Conflicting 'Ages' of Tertiary Basalt and Contained Fossilised Wood, Crinum, Central Queensland, Australia" at answersingenesis.org

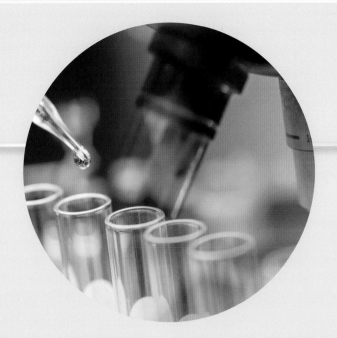

THREE MAJOR ASSUMPTIONS

When testing a hypothesis, it is vital to remove as many assumptions as possible. The more assumptions present, the less certainty we have in the conclusions that are reached.

Scientists may strive to eliminate these assumptions, but it is often impossible to remove them all. For example, the RATE* research group conducted carbon-14 tests on diamonds. Due to their unique properties, diamonds are highly resistant to contaminating factors, eliminating the third assumption (see infographic).
The testing yielded much younger dates than those conventionally assigned to diamonds.

*RATE: A team of experts who met from 1997–2005 to study radioactive isotopes in relation to the age of the earth.

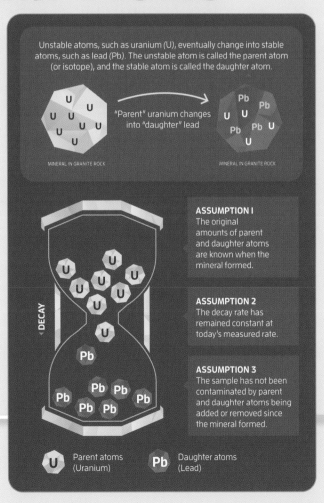

Unstable atoms, such as uranium (U), eventually change into stable atoms, such as lead (Pb). The unstable atom is called the parent atom (or isotope), and the stable atom is called the daughter atom.

"Parent" uranium changes into "daughter" lead

MINERAL IN GRANITE ROCK

MINERAL IN GRANITE ROCK

DECAY

ASSUMPTION 1
The original amounts of parent and daughter atoms are known when the mineral formed.

ASSUMPTION 2
The decay rate has remained constant at today's measured rate.

ASSUMPTION 3
The sample has not been contaminated by parent and daughter atoms being added or removed since the mineral formed.

U — Parent atoms (Uranium)

Pb — Daughter atoms (Lead)

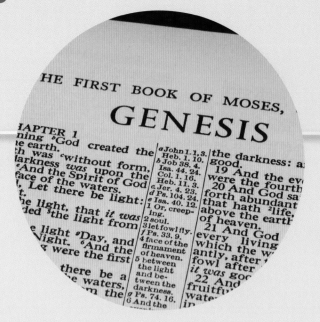

MOST RELIABLE DATING METHOD

Without question, consulting a reliable eyewitness is the best method to discover the age of something. For example, a man can accurately determine his age based on his birth certificate because it was signed by reliable eyewitnesses of his birth. The Bible provides God's eyewitness testimony of how and when He created the earth.

> God has always existed, knows all things, and cannot lie. Therefore, His Word is the infallible source of information regarding the age of the earth.

"I, the LORD, speak the truth, declaring things that are right." **(Isaiah 45:19)**

"Your word is truth." **(John 17:17)**

All Scripture is God-breathed, and it is profitable for teaching, for reproof, for correction, and for instruction in righteousness, so that the man of God may be complete, equipped for every good work. **(2 Timothy 3:16–17)**

. . . it is impossible for God to lie. . . **(Hebrews 6:18)**

UNITY & DIVERSITY
ANIMAL KINDS

VARIATION WITHIN A KIND IS NOT EVOLUTION

This wall illustrates the biblical creationist concept of created kinds, an interpretation of data consistent with the biblical record. There can be many related species within a kind, but each kind is uniquely created and unrelated to other kinds. This variation within a kind may sound like evolution, but the two paint very different pictures.

For example, according to naturalistic ideas, cats, dogs, seals, and all other members of the order Carnivora are considered related, having evolved from a common ancestor. By contrast, biblical creationists consider Carnivora a useful category but believe it is composed of many separate created kinds. The design features that unify carnivorans as a group are therefore seen as indicating functional similarities instead of true relatedness.

FELIDAE: CAT KIND

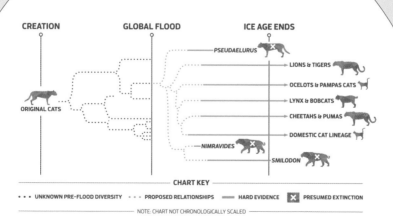

The cat kind is represented today by around 40 different species, such as lions, servals, cheetahs, and house cats. Approximately 60 breeds of domestic cats are currently recognized.

OTARIIDAE: EARED SEAL KIND

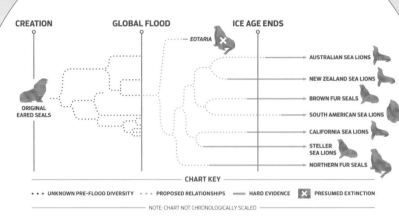

Eared seals are currently represented by 15 species, including various fur seals and sea lions. While resembling true or earless seals and walruses, the three groups are likely not members of the same kind.

CANIDAE: DOG KIND

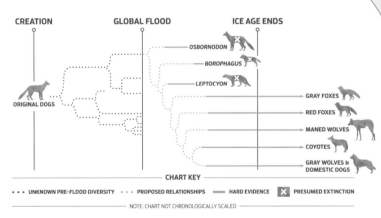

Consisting today of about 35 species, such as foxes, wolves, and jackals, the potential for variation within this kind is best seen in domestic dogs: over 300 breeds derive from this single subspecies, *Canis lupus domesticus*.

ONE RACE, ONE BLOOD
THE HUMAN KIND

CREATION: GOD CREATES HUMANKIND IN HIS IMAGE

ADAM & EVE

GLOBAL FLOOD: GOD JUDGES HUMANKIND FOR THEIR REBELLION

NOAH & WIFE

BABEL: GOD SCATTERS HUMANKIND

HUMAN DIVERSITY

The human kind apparently has a more limited expression of forms than many animal kinds, but the range of physical diversity expressed among humans during the Ice Age seems much greater than it is today. Biblical creationists see this broad spectrum of variance as evidence that archaic humans likely possessed a much higher potential for variation than modern humans. Debates persist regarding how these ancient people should be biologically classified. Physical variations notwithstanding, all archaic and anatomically modern humans are equal expressions of the human kind— fellow descendants of Adam created in the image of God.

HISTORICAL CONTEXT

The oldest definitive human evidences are known from sites located a significant distance from Babel. These artifacts and remains are buried in layers that biblical creationist geologists generally consider post-Flood but pre-Ice Age. This indicates that even the oldest known human sites are post-Babel.

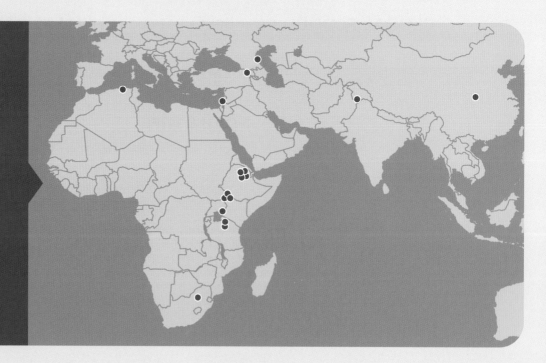

Dispersion of human sites by the early Ice Age.

THE GREAT APE KIND

Variation within kinds is seen across the animal kingdom, and this is certainly the case with great apes. Likely distinct from gibbons or lesser apes (Family: Hylobatidae), this kind is represented today by three genera divided into seven species. Additionally, over 50 extinct species are known to have existed before and during the Ice Age. Despite this variation, members of the group have always been distinct from people. Fossil evidence has demonstrated that even the australopithecines shared a greater likeness to other apes than humans. Therefore, the great apes are treated here according to the older convention of placing them in their own family, Pongidae, rather than the newer convention of placing them in the human family, Hominidae.

LUCY

Discovered in the Awash Valley of Ethiopia in 1974 and conventionally dated at 3.2 million years, "Lucy" is the fourth-known, most complete, and most famous specimen of *Australopithecus afarensis*. Despite usually being depicted as very humanlike, Lucy's species is classified as non-human.

From a biblical creationist perspective, her kind is regarded as completely unrelated to people—the two having existed as separate kinds since the beginning. Though australopithecines have some distinctive traits, they most closely resemble the great apes, such as gorillas, chimpanzees, and orangutans. Thus, Lucy was a member of an ape kind instead of a human relative.

WHO ARE LUCY'S RELATIVES? THE GREAT APES

APELING MORPHOLOGY: LITTLE APES, LITTLE DIFFERENCE

Displayed here are three ape skulls from specimens under five years of age. On the left is the skull of "Taung Child," an *Australopithecus africanus* and the first australopithecine to be discovered. In the middle is a chimpanzee (*Pan troglodytes*). On the right is "Selam," likely an *Australopithecus afarensis*—Lucy's species. Notice that the similarities between these specimens extend well beyond a vague likeness of proportions to specific shared traits of the teeth, jaws, nasal openings, and eye cavities. And while distinct enough to be considered different species, the similarities are what we would expect if they are related animals. Most significantly, they have much more in common with each other than they do with humans.

AUSTRALOPITHECUS AFARENSIS
MALE

STATUS:
PRESUMED EXTINCT

DISTRIBUTION:
EASTERN AFRICA

ARDIPITHECUS RAMIDUS
FEMALE

STATUS:
PRESUMED EXTINCT

DISTRIBUTION:
EASTERN AFRICA

PARANTHROPUS BOISEI
MALE

STATUS:
PRESUMED EXTINCT

DISTRIBUTION:
EASTERN AFRICA

BONOBO
FEMALE

STATUS:
LIVING SPECIES

DISTRIBUTION:
CENTRAL AFRICA

LOWLAND GORILLA
FEMALE

STATUS:
LIVING SPECIES

DISTRIBUTION:
CENTRAL AFRICA

BORNEO ORANGUTAN
FEMALE

STATUS:
LIVING SPECIES

DISTRIBUTION:
EASTERN AFRICA

"SELAM"
AUSTRALOPITHECUS AFARENSIS

STATUS:
PRESUMED EXTINCT

DISTRIBUTION:
EASTERN AFRICA

CHIMPANZEE
PAN TROGLODYTES
STATUS:
LIVING SPECIES

DISTRIBUTION:
WESTERN & CENTRAL
AFRICA

"TAUNG CHILD"
AUSTRALOPITHECUS AFRICANUS
STATUS:
PRESUMED EXTINCT

DISTRIBUTION:
SOUTHERN AFRICA

WHOSE FOOTPRINTS ARE THESE?

A major reason Lucy and other australopithecines are depicted as very humanlike originated with the discovery of fossilized footprints in Laetoli, Tanzania. At the time, the tracks represented the earliest known humanlike footprints in the world, being conventionally dated to 3.7 million years old. The 75-foot-long (23 m) pre-Ice Age trackway was made when at least three individuals walked across wet volcanic ash. The sun quickly baked the footprints which were then gently infilled with succeeding layers of ash. The gait and foot anatomy of the trackmakers is indistinguishable from humans.

NATURALISTIC
EVOLUTIONIST WORLDVIEW

▸ The best examples of Lucy's species are known from the Afar region of Ethiopia—hence the species name *afarensis*—but the prototypical specimen, a partial lower jawbone, was discovered in Tanzania only five miles away in the same formation as the footprints. After several more specimens were discovered in Ethiopia, the species was formally described and subsequently proposed as the most likely source of the tracks. According to current conventional estimates, the footprints predate the earliest known remains of *Homo*, the human genus, by nearly one million years. Therefore, evolutionists automatically disregard the idea that humans made the tracks.

BIBLICAL
CREATIONIST WORLDVIEW

▸ Since the Bible indicates the original people and land animals were created on the same day several thousand years ago, biblical creationists believe the Laetoli tracks were made during human history. The footprints are practically identical in shape to some early Ice Age tracks from Ileret, Kenya—ones universally attributed to archaic humans (pictured below). More complete australopithecine specimens (such as "Little Foot") have demonstrated that their feet were more ape-like than evolutionists anticipated. Also, their hip designs reveal that they had a different gait from that of humans. Consequently, it seems that humans rather than australopithecines created the Laetoli tracks.

WHICH FOOTPRINT BEST MATCHES **THE LAETOLI TRACKS?**

AUSTRALOPITHECINE FOOTPRINT

ARCHAIC HUMAN FOOTPRINT

PROJECTED LAETOLI FOOTPRINT

ART AND PERSPECTIVE

▶ This head is cast from the same mold as the head on the Lucy sculpture to the left. It represents what Lucy's head may have looked like with only flesh. **Artistic decisions can strongly influence how we view Lucy.** Was she more human-like or ape-like? Below are three examples based on different art directions.

"Ape-man"
Lucy

"Gorilla"
Lucy

"Orangutan"
Lucy

THE POWER OF PERSPECTIVE

▶ Art is communication. Even when words are absent, it has a great capacity to convey meaning. When you look at a piece of art, remember that it speaks for the artist who crafted it to tell a story.

Consider these depictions of australopithecine heads, cast from the same mold as the "Lucy" figure. Despite looking very different from one another, their sculpted details are identical. Only arbitrary details set them apart—things like hair, eye, and skin colors, as well as hair length and coverage.

Whether filling in missing bits of skull, surveying a bony surface for muscle attachment points, or choosing skin tones based on specimen location, degrees of assumption attend every stage of reconstruction. Ironically, the more superficial elements—things that

represent the biggest unknowns—are often most effective in conveying a broader narrative.

For example, artists who wish to communicate that australopithecines were human relatives usually add human eyes and hair patterns. Those who wish to show that australopithecines were more like other apes will take inspiration from familiar varieties like gorillas, chimpanzees, or orangutans.

There is nothing wrong with using art to communicate. But these examples demonstrate at least two important things: how art can be used to shape public opinions, and how preconceived ideas can significantly impact art. Art, like the tongue or written words, can be a powerful tool for good or ill.

Art always speaks, so ask yourself what it is saying.

WHY AM I HERE?

NATURALISTIC
EVOLUTIONIST
WORLDVIEW

▸ We are just a cosmic accident, the product of time and chance.

> *"There is no higher purpose. It's left to us. We must create our purpose. That's the only meaning we have in this universe."* —Michael Shermer[1]

> *"Yes, secularism does propose a physical and purposeless universe, and many (but not all) of us accept the notion that our sense of self is a neuronal illusion. But although the universe is purposeless, our lives aren't. This conflation of a purposeless universe (i.e., one not created for a specific reason) with purposeless human lives is a trick that the faithful use to make atheism seem nihilistic and dark. But we make our own purposes, and they're real."* —Jerry Coyne[2]

[1]Michael Shermer said this in an interview with Lee Strobel. See Lee Strobel, *The Case for Miracles* (Grand Rapids, MI: Zondervan, 2018), p. 46.

[2]Jerry A. Coyne, "Douthat on the Rampage Against Secularism, Gets It All Wrong" at https://whyevolutionistrue.wordpress.com/2013/12/23/douthat-on-the-rampage-against-secularism-gets-it-all-wrong. Emphasis in original.

BIBLICAL
CREATIONIST
WORLDVIEW

▸ God created man in His image and gave man authority over this world. We are made to love God and one another and reflect God's glory to this world.

> *"God created man in His own image...Be fruitful and multiply...rule over the fish of the sea, the birds of the air, and every living thing that moves on the earth."* —Genesis 1:27–28

> *"You shall love the Lord your God with all your heart, soul, mind, and strength...You shall love your neighbor as yourself."* —Mark 12:30–31

WHY DO PEOPLE SUFFER AND DIE?

NATURALISTIC
EVOLUTIONIST
WORLDVIEW

▸ Death, suffering, and disease have always been part of the evolutionary history on our planet.

"During the minute that it takes me to compose this sentence, thousands of animals are being eaten alive, many others are running for their lives, whimpering with fear, others are slowly being devoured from within by rasping parasites, thousands of all kinds are dying of starvation, thirst, and disease. It must be so. If there ever is a time of plenty, this very fact will automatically lead to an increase in the population until the natural state of starvation and misery is restored... In a universe of blind physical forces and genetic replication, some people are going to get hurt, and other people are going to get lucky; and you won't find any rhyme or reason to it, nor any justice."—Richard Dawkins[1]

[1]Richard Dawkins, *River Out of Eden* (New York: Basic Books, 1995), pp. 132–133.

BIBLICAL
CREATIONIST
WORLDVIEW

▸ God made a perfect world, but man's rebellion brought death, suffering, and disease into this world.

"God saw everything He had made, and it was very good."—Genesis 1:31

"...cursed is the ground because of you; in painful toil you shall eat of it all the days of your life. It will produce thorns and thistles for you, and you shall eat the plants of the field. By the sweat of your face you shall eat bread until you return to the ground, because from it you were taken; for you are dust, and to dust you will return."—Genesis 3:17–19

"Just as sin entered the world through one man and death through sin, and so death spread to all men..."—Romans 5:12

"The last enemy to be destroyed is death."—I Corinthians 15:26

HOW DO WE KNOW RIGHT AND WRONG?

NATURALISTIC
EVOLUTIONIST
WORLDVIEW

▸ The individual or the society decides what is right and wrong. This can vary depending upon the individual or the society.

"Morality, or more strictly, our belief in morality, is merely an adaptation put in place to further our reproductive ends. Hence the basis of ethics does not lie in God's will or in the metaphorical roots of evolution or any other part of the framework of the universe. In an important sense, ethics as we understand it is an illusion fobbed off on us by our genes to get us to cooperate. It is without external grounding. Ethics is produced by evolution, but not justified by it, because, like Macbeth's dagger, it serves a powerful purpose without existing in substance."—Michael Ruse and E.O. Wilson[1]

[1] Michael Ruse and E.O. Wilson, "The Evolution of Ethics" in James E. Huchingson, ed., *Religion and the Natural Sciences: The Range of Engagement* (Orlando, FL: Harcourt Brace, 1993), p. 310.

BIBLICAL
CREATIONIST
WORLDVIEW

▸ God is the standard of what is right and wrong—morality is rooted in the perfectly good nature of the unchanging, all-powerful God of the Bible.

"God is light, and in Him there is no darkness at all."—I John 1:5

"Again Jesus spoke to them, saying, 'I am the light of the world. Whoever follows me will not walk in darkness, but will have the light of life.'"—John 8:12

"He has told you, O man, what is good; and what does the Lord require of you but to do justice, and to love kindness, and to walk humbly with your God?"—Micah 6:8

IS THERE ANY HOPE?

NATURALISTIC
EVOLUTIONIST
WORLDVIEW

▸ There is no hope of overcoming suffering, disease, and death. Someday you will die, and your body will rot. There is no afterlife. Every person, whether kind or murderous, will cease to exist with no final justice. Ultimately, life is meaningless.

"The universe we observe has precisely the properties we should expect if there is, at bottom, no design, no purpose, no evil and no good, nothing but blind, pitiless indifference."—Richard Dawkins[1]

"The Earth is just a speck of sand in the universe. And there's no cavalry coming over the hill to rescue it."
—Bill Nye[2]

[1] Richard Dawkins, *River Out of Eden* (New York: Basic Books, 1995), p. 133.

[2] Pat Whitney, "Nye: We Must All Save the Earth," *Madison Courier* (Madison, IN), February 21, 2009.

BIBLICAL
CREATIONIST
WORLDVIEW

▸ God put on human flesh, stepping into history as a man, the Lord Jesus Christ. He suffered and died to pay the penalty for our sins. Those who believe in Him will be forgiven and live eternally with God.

"For God so loved the world, that He gave His only begotten Son, that whoever believes in Him should not perish but have eternal life."—John 3:16

"Look, the dwelling place of God is with man... And God will wipe away every tear from their eyes, and death shall be no more. There will be no more mourning, crying, or pain, for the former things have passed away."—Revelation 21:3–4

WHAT HAPPENS WHEN I DIE?

NATURALISTIC
EVOLUTIONIST
WORLDVIEW

▶ There is no afterlife for anyone. All people will eventually die and cease to exist.

"I regard the brain as a computer which will stop working when its components fail. There is no heaven or afterlife for broken down computers; that is a fairy story for people afraid of the dark." —Stephen Hawking[1]

"There are no gods, no purposes, and no goal-directed forces of any kind. There is no life after death. When I die, I am absolutely certain that I am going to be dead." —William Provine[2]

[1] Ian Sample, "Stephen Hawking: 'There Is No Heaven; It's a Fairy Story,'" *Guardian* (United Kingdom), May 15, 2011, https://www.theguardian.com/science/2011/may/15/stephen-hawking-interview-there-is-no-heaven.

[2] William Provine and Phillip Johnson, Darwinism: Science or Naturalistic Philosophy? The Debate at Stanford University (Berkeley, CA: Regents of the University of California, 1994), DVD.

BIBLICAL
CREATIONIST
WORLDVIEW

▶ Every person has been created to live forever—eternal life with the Creator or eternal separation from Him in the lake of fire.

"Truly, truly, I say to you, whoever hears My word and believes Him who sent me has eternal life. He will not come into judgment, but has passed from death to life."—John 5:24

"If anyone's name was not found written in the book of life, that man was thrown into the lake of fire." —Revelation 20:15

WILL JUSTICE BE SERVED?

NATURALISTIC **EVOLUTIONIST WORLDVIEW**	BIBLICAL **CREATIONIST WORLDVIEW**

▸ Ultimately, there is no justice. Yes, some people will pay for certain crimes in the present world, but other criminals will get away with their crimes. The mass murderer suffers the same fate as the most loving and kind person.

"This concept of the afterlife really functions as a substitute for wisdom. It functions as a substitute for really absorbing our predicament, which is that everyone is going to die; there are circumstances that are just catastrophically unfair; evil sometimes wins and injustice sometimes wins, and that the only justice we are going to find in the world is the justice we make."—Sam Harris[1]

▸ God is perfect in His love, and perfect love demands perfect justice. Justice will ultimately be served. Those who have received forgiveness of their sins through faith in the resurrected Savior's sacrificial death on their behalf will inherit eternal life. Those who reject Christ's payment of sins will suffer eternally for their rebellion against God.

"Do not marvel at this, for an hour is coming when all who are in the tombs will hear his voice and come out, those who have done good to the resurrection of life, and those who have done evil to the resurrection of judgment."—John 5:28–29

[1]"Is There an Afterlife? - Christopher Hitchens, Sam Harris, David Wolpe, Bradley Artson Shavit," YouTube, December 29, 2011, video, 1:37:54, https://www.youtube.com/watch?v=UjKj92b9YO4.

HOW WILL IT ALL END?

NATURALISTIC
EVOLUTIONIST
WORLDVIEW

▸ The universe will eventually undergo a "heat death" when all usable energy has been used up. All life will end. Indeed, all chemical, biological, and physical processes will cease.

"...we don't particularly welcome the idea of the annihilation of either ourselves as individuals, the party will go on and we'll have left, and we're not coming back, or, the entropic heat death of the universe. We don't like the idea, but there's a good deal of evidence to suggest that is what's gonna happen."—Christopher Hitchens[1]

BIBLICAL
CREATIONIST
WORLDVIEW

▸ This world will be burned up and the Lord will create a new heavens and a new earth that will be filled with righteousness.

"...as you look forward to the day of God... That day will bring about the destruction of the heavens by fire, and the elements will melt in the heat. But in keeping with His promise we are looking forward to a new heaven and a new earth, where righteousness dwells." —2 Peter 3:12–13

[1] Biola University, "Does God Exist? William Lane Craig vs. Christopher Hitchens," YouTube, September 28, 2014, video, 2:27:42, https://www.youtube.com/watch?v=0tYm41hb48o.

BIBLICAL AUTHORITY

GOD'S WORD IS OUR AUTHORITY

Our view of the Bible models the approach set by the Lord Jesus Christ. When confronted with questions, Jesus frequently replied by citing Scripture, introducing His responses with phrases such as "Have you not read..." or "It is written...." His example demonstrates that He viewed Scripture as being historically accurate and authoritative for every area of life.

GOD DEMONSTRATES HIS AUTHORITY

The God of the Bible is the Creator of heaven and earth and Lord over all. In Exodus 6:3, He told Moses that His name is YHWH (יהוה in Hebrew), which most biblical scholars believe is pronounced Yahweh. English Bibles often translate this word as LORD—the use of small capitals distinguishes it from another Hebrew term translated as Lord.

THE BIBLE FREQUENTLY DECLARES THAT YAHWEH IS GREATER THAN ALL OTHER GODS.

"For Yahweh is a great God, a great King above all gods." **(Psalm 95:3)**

"Yahweh, who is like You among the gods? Who is like You, majestic in holiness, revered with praises, performing wonders?" **(2 Chronicles 2:5)**

The people of the nations around Israel worshipped many gods and represented them with idols that they made, but Yahweh called His people to be different. God gave the Ten Commandments to Israel at Mt. Sinai, and the first two laws focused on this subject.

"You shall have no other gods before me." **(Exodus 20:3)**

"You shall not make for yourself a carved image...you shall not bow down to them or serve them." **(Exodus 20:4–5)**

Throughout the Bible God demonstrated His supremacy over the gods of the nations. This exhibit features different periods in biblical history, and in each era Yahweh proved His authority over all powers in heaven and earth.

DEPICTING THE **WORLD OF THE BIBLE**

When thinking about biblical people, places, and cultures, there is a strong tendency to overgeneralize these as a one-size-fits-all concept known as "Bible times," in which each character wore a robe, each man had a beard, etc. But the reality is that the Bible is a collection of books written during many historical periods and from a wide variety of backgrounds throughout the Mediterranean and Middle East. Cultures are dynamic and change frequently, and the cultures in the Bible are no exception. The world that Abraham knew is not the same one that David knew, or that Paul knew. This room reflects some of those differences and distinctions, from the structured and consistent style of ancient Egypt to the elegant and innovative style of the first century Greco-Roman world.

ARCHITECTURE

Bright colors and bold designs embellished the monumental structures of the ancient world, often depicting regional animals and plants, such as the lotus flower. Over the centuries, these designs were modified as they spread from one culture to another. For example, the Ionic capital used in architecture around the world today has its origin in ancient Phoenicia, where its early shape, the Aeolic capital, imitated the date palm that grows along the Mediterranean coast.

Examples of various capitals, including Ionic (left), Aeolic (center), and Egyptian (right).

CLOTHING

Clothing styles never remained stagnant. For example, the Israelites' clothing constantly changed and adjusted to the cultures around them, while mostly remaining true to the Mosaic law against mixing fibers. All of the biblical heroes featured in this exhibit are dressed in outfits consistent with their respective times.

Sketches of what David (left) and Rahab (right) may have worn

SYMBOLS

Symbols and what they mean to different people change throughout history. Their meanings can become something that was never intended by the original designer. For example, the signet rings of Hezekiah, used to officiate documents, featured either an Egyptian scarab beetle or a winged sun-disk. The scarab beetle and sun-disk were worshipped in Egypt as gods, but in other lands, including Hezekiah's kingdom, this imagery probably symbolized royal power and authority instead of pagan worship.

Hezekiah may have worn the Egyptian scarab beetle medallion (left) and winged sun-disk signet ring (right).

GOD'S WORD IS...

AUTHORITATIVE

The words of the Bible ultimately come from the God who knows everything and cannot lie. Therefore, it is authoritative in every subject it addresses, whether it is discussing scientific issues, history, geography, or any matter of faith and practice.

The fact that the Bible is authoritative does not mean that every verse is directly applicable to every believer or that later instructions cannot supersede earlier ones. For example, God instructed Abraham to move to a new land, but this does not mean that all believers must do this. Also, the Lord told the first man and woman that they were to eat vegetation, but after the Flood, He told Noah that man was now permitted to eat meat.

GOD'S WORD IS...

WITHOUT ERROR

Since the Bible is the Word of God, and since God cannot make mistakes, then it follows that the Bible does not contain errors. This teaching, known as the doctrine of inerrancy, applies only to the original manuscripts and the copies insofar as they accurately represent the originals.

The doctrine of inerrancy does not mean the Bible never records false statements. For example, Genesis 3:4 truthfully recounts the serpent's lie ("You will not surely die"), and much of Job consists of faithful retellings of the words of Job's friends who frequently made erroneous claims. These types of statements do not mean that the Bible contains errors. Rather, the Bible inerrantly reports false assertions made by certain individuals.

GOD'S WORD IS...

DIVINELY INSPIRED

"God-breathed." This term is used in 2 Timothy 3:16 to describe all Scripture. This means that God moved and guided the authors of the Bible as they wrote so that what was penned can truly be called God's Word. At the same time, this process allowed the writers to utilize their own styles, personalities, and experiences.

The doctrine of inspiration does not mean that God dictated each word to the writer, as some have supposed. Also, it permits a later writer to update certain details. For example, Joshua is believed to have been the primary author of the book bearing his name. However, certain statements were likely added later. Joshua 11:21 mentions the mountains of Judah and the mountains of Israel, which seems to imply this verse was written after the kingdom divided following the reign of Solomon.

THE AGE **OF THE EARTH**

DOES SCRIPTURE REVEAL EARTH'S AGE?

The Bible states that earth was made on Day One. Adam was made on Day Six, and his son Seth was born 130 years later. By adding the figures in the genealogies in Genesis 5 and 11, we discover that approximately 2,000 years passed before Abraham. Abraham lived roughly 2,000 years before Jesus Christ. And there have been about 2,000 years from Jesus until now.

The idea that the earth was created about 4,000 years before Christ is nothing new. Throughout church history, people have attempted to calculate the age of the earth based on the Bible.

NAME	APPROXIMATE DATE OF WRITING	DATE OF CREATION
Julius Africanus	AD 221	5502 BC
Marianus Scotus	AD 1080	4192 BC
Martin Luther	AD 1540	3960 BC
Philip Melanchthon	AD 1550	3963 BC
James Ussher	AD 1658	4004 BC

A couple of factors account for most of the differences in the range of dates given. First, one must choose which manuscript tradition to base the calculations on. The Greek translation of the Old Testament, known as the Septuagint, includes an additional 1,250–1,380 years in Genesis 5 and 11. Second, the meaning of certain passages is debated. For example, were the Israelites in Egypt for 215 years or 430 years?

Whichever options one favors, there is simply no legitimate way to make the Bible teach the earth is tens of thousands of years old, let alone millions or billions.

ADAM   SETH

ARE THERE GAPS IN THE GENESIS GENEALOGIES?

Some Christians have attempted to add long periods of time to the Bible by asserting that gaps of indeterminate length could be added to the genealogies of Genesis 5 and 11.

We know gaps exist in certain biblical genealogies, such as Matthew 1, but gaps of time cannot be added to the Genesis 5 and 11 genealogies because the text explains how old each person was when their son was born. For example, Adam was 130 years old when Seth was born, and Seth was 105 when Enosh was born. So even if it were possible to insert an extra generation or two in between Adam and Seth it would not change the timeline—Adam was still 130 years old when Seth was born.

THE BIBLE IS SCIENTIFICALLY ACCURATE

The Bible is not a science textbook, but it is accurate whenever it touches on scientific matters, such as the following:

GEOLOGY

Abundant evidence for the global Flood described in Genesis 7–8 is found around the world in the many layers of fossil-bearing sediments that stretch across continents.

BIOLOGY

God made plants and animals according to their kind. There is diversity within each kind, but one kind has never given rise to another kind.

Science textbooks frequently change as new discoveries are made and hypotheses are formed, but God's Word remains the same and is true from beginning to end.

THE BIBLE IS HISTORICALLY ACCURATE

One of the many aspects that sets the Bible apart from other "holy books" is that its truth claims are rooted in history. The truth of its overarching message depends upon whether the episodes it describes truly took place (1 Corinthians 15:14–17). For example, the Bible reports that its central figure, Jesus Christ, spoke to huge crowds in first-century Israel before being killed in a public execution. So the claims of Christianity can be examined historically, unlike the many faiths that make no attempt to ground their claims in history.

The historical reliability of the Bible has been scrutinized like no other book, yet centuries of critical and skeptical attacks have failed to repudiate Scripture. In fact, most of the negative criticism launched against the Bible is based on one's philosophical presuppositions rather than the findings of archaeological and historical investigations, which have repeatedly confirmed biblical accounts.

After a distinguished career as president of Hebrew Union College, renowned archaeologist Dr. Nelson Glueck wrote the following:

"It may be stated categorically that no archaeological discovery has ever controverted a Biblical reference. Scores of archaeological findings have been made which confirm in clear outline or exact detail historical statements in the Bible. And, by the same token, proper evaluation of Biblical description has often led to amazing discoveries."

Dr. Nelson Glueck, *Rivers in the Desert,* (New York: Farrar, Straus, and Cudahy, 1959), 136.

EXAMPLES OF HISTORICAL ACCURACY

This exhibit highlights archaeological confirmation of certain details related to key figures from various eras described in Scripture.

JOSEPH

THE BIBLICAL RECORD

Joseph was born in ancient Syria while his father, Jacob, worked for Laban the Syrian. When Joseph was young, his family moved to the land of Canaan and eventually settled in Hebron. The favored son of his father, Joseph was sold into slavery by his brothers who grew envious of him. Joseph wound up in Egypt as a slave of Potiphar, an officer of Pharaoh.

Falsely accused of sexual assault by Potiphar's wife, Joseph spent years in prison before interpreting two of Pharaoh's dreams and being elevated to become the second most powerful person in Egypt. During the seven-year famine that devastated the land, Joseph provided for his father and eleven brothers, and they moved their families to Goshen in Egypt where their descendants, the Israelites, were eventually enslaved.

יהוה

YAHWEH VS. THE EGYPTIAN GODS

Centuries after Joseph first entered Egypt as a slave, God delivered the Israelites from their bondage in Egypt. The Lord told Moses that He would execute judgment on "all the gods of Egypt" (Exodus 12:12). When bringing an end to the plague of frogs, Moses told Pharaoh that it would happen at the requested time so "that you may know that there is no one like Yahweh our God" (Exodus 8:10). The following chart gives some examples of how the plagues demonstrated Yahweh's power over the Egyptian gods.

#	PLAGUE	EGYPTIAN DEITY	DOMAIN
1	Nile turned to blood Fish died	Hapi Hatmeyt	The god of the Nile The fish-goddess
2	Frogs	Hekt	Frog-headed goddess of fertility
5	Livestock	Hathor	Cow-headed goddess of love
6	Boils	Im-Hotep	The god of healing
8	Locusts	Senehem	Locust-headed god of harvest
9	Darkness	Amon-Re	Sun god
10	Firstborn	Pharaoh and Pharaoh's son Isis	Son of the sun god Protector of children

THE ARCHAEOLOGICAL RECORD

CULTURE: Canaanite | **ERA:** Middle Bronze Age | **FEATURED ELEMENT:** Egyptian cow goddess Hathor

3D rendering of the Tell el-Dab'a site, including a Syrian-style palace and houses, as well as graves and a tomb
3D render courtesy of Patterns of Evidence, LLC

IS THIS JOSEPH'S PALACE?

Ongoing excavations at Tell el-Dab'a in Egypt have revealed a once prosperous settlement inhabited by *Aamu* (Asiatics), a term describing foreign people groups from the north and east. These non-native shepherds built Syrian-style houses and buried their dead in traditional Asiatic graves with perfume, imported jewelry, Syro-Palestinian weapons, and other luxury items. The evidence mirrors the biblical description of Joseph's Syrian family prospering for many years in the delta region of Egypt (Exodus 1:7; Deuteronomy 26:5).

Asiatic graves and a tomb believed to be Joseph's
3D render courtesy of Patterns of Evidence, LLC

The earliest Asiatic settlement at Tell el-Dab'a was established toward the end of Egypt's powerful 12th Dynasty. Pharaohs of this period constructed a giant irrigation system which includes the canal known today as the *Bahr Yussef* (the Waterway of Joseph). At the same time, there is evidence that native Egyptian governors suddenly fell from power. During the seven-year famine, Joseph purchased all the land, livestock, and people of Egypt for Pharaoh (Genesis 47:13–26). This is consistent with the sudden fall from power of many Egyptian governors.

In 1986, fragments of a limestone statue, representing a powerful Asiatic official, were discovered in the earliest cemetery at Tell el-Dab'a. The statue featured a throw-stick—the symbol of an Asiatic—and a red and black striped cloak, reminiscent of the colorful coat given to Joseph by his father (Genesis 37:3).

Fragments (*left*) and 3D render (*right*) of an Asiatic official
Photos courtesy of David Rohl, 3D render courtesy of Patterns of Evidence, LLC

Patterns of Evidence DVDs are available in the bookstore.

Based on these and many other details about the tomb and its surroundings, some scholars believe this statue may be a representation of Joseph.

54

RAHAB

THE BIBLICAL RECORD

Following the Exodus, the Israelites wandered in the wilderness for 40 years before finally entering the land God had promised to give them (Genesis 17:7–8; Joshua 3:17). The first city they encountered was Jericho.

Two spies sent by Joshua met a harlot named Rahab who hid them on the roof of her house, which was located on the wall of the city. She explained that her people feared Israel because of what their God had done to the Egyptians and the kings on the other side of the Jordan River. The spies agreed to spare her and her family if she marked her window with a scarlet rope.

As God instructed, the Israelites marched around Jericho for seven days. The Lord miraculously knocked down the walls, and Jericho was defeated. Rahab was spared and became an ancestor of King David and the Lord Jesus Christ.

YAHWEH VS. THE CANAANITE GODS

Through Moses, the Lord repeatedly warned the Israelites to refrain from chasing after pagan gods. Prior to Jericho, God judged those who worshiped a golden calf (Exodus 32:4–6) or Baal of Peor (Numbers 25:2–3).

After conquering Jericho and taking possession of the promised land, the Israelites acknowledged that Yahweh was the God who freed them from Egypt and drove out the wicked peoples of the land, whose gods could not protect them. The Israelites vowed that they would serve Yahweh because He was their God (Joshua 24:16–18).

Sadly, the Israelites failed to drive out all the Canaanites, Hittites, Amorites, Perizzites, and Hivites. They married people from these pagan nations and worshiped their gods—the Baals and Asherahs (Judges 3:5–7). Throughout the book of Judges, whenever Israel practiced idolatry, God allowed another nation to oppress them—He did not grant them victory over these groups while they were unfaithful to Him. But whenever Israel cried out to Yahweh, He demonstrated His power over the other gods by sending a judge to rescue His people.

THE ARCHAEOLOGICAL RECORD

CULTURE: Canaanite | **ERA:** 15th century BC | **FEATURED ELEMENT:** Pagan gods Baal and Asherah

The ruins of Jericho (Tell es-Sultan)

IS TELL ES-SULTAN RAHAB'S JERICHO?

Tell es-Sultan is the famous ruin identified as the ancient city of Jericho, one of the oldest cities in the world, and it provides compelling evidence consistent with the biblical account of the city's destruction.

Multiple excavations from 1907 through 2014 have confirmed the sudden destruction of the well-fortified Middle Bronze Age city, as recorded in the Bible (Joshua 6). The city's massive mud-brick walls completely collapsed and fell outward to the base of the mound. Some excavators suggest Jericho was destroyed by a powerful earthquake. This evidence fits the biblical account of the fortified walls falling in dramatic fashion, allowing the Israelite army to climb up over the rubble into the doomed city (Joshua 6:20).

A heavy burn layer, several feet thick, covers the ruins. Jars brimming with charred grain confirm the Bible's report that the Israelites burned the city shortly after the spring harvest during the Jordan River's flood-stage (Joshua 3:15). It also corroborates the Bible's claim that the Israelites only plundered items made of gold, silver, bronze, or iron. Everything else of value was burned with the city, including the intact food stores (Joshua 6:19, 24).

Additionally, the earliest excavations in 1907–1909 found evidence for the survival of a small portion of the north, lower city wall with houses built against it. This matches the biblical account of how Rahab helped the spies escape the city through a window on the city's outer wall (Joshua 2:15).

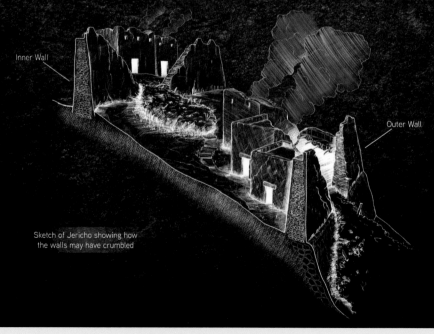

Inner Wall

Outer Wall

Sketch of Jericho showing how the walls may have crumbled

DAVID

THE BIBLICAL RECORD

David is one of the most famous figures in the Bible. As a young man, he killed the mighty Philistine Goliath with a sling and a stone. He flourished as a military commander under King Saul until the king sought to kill him because he grew envious of David's successes and popularity among the people.

Following Saul's death, David became the king of Judah and eventually ruled all of Israel, and it quickly grew into a powerful nation. His public achievements were marred by personal failures, particularly when he committed adultery with Bathsheba and plotted to have her husband killed in battle. Yet this man after God's own heart soon repented of those sins and ended up writing nearly half of the psalms in the Bible and made preparations for his son Solomon to build the first Jewish temple.

YAHWEH VS. THE PHILISTINE GODS

A few decades before David, the Philistines captured the Ark of the Covenant and placed it in the temple of their god, Dagon. God showed His power over the Philistine god by causing Dagon's statue to fall down before the Ark on two consecutive nights. On the second evening, the head and hands of Dagon's statue were broken off (1 Samuel 5:1–5).

Goliath reviled Israel's God and cursed David by the names of the Philistine gods. David told Goliath that God would give him the victory so that all the people may know that there is a God in Israel (1 Samuel 17:43–46).

Yahweh richly blessed Israel because of David's commitment to Him, turning Israel into the most prosperous nation on earth during Solomon's reign. However, Solomon's many wives led him into the worship of false gods, such as the Sidonian goddess Astarte, the Ammonite god Milcom, and the Moabite god Chemosh. God told Solomon that He would split the nation in two because of Solomon's worship of other gods (1 Kings 11:1–13).

THE ARCHAEOLOGICAL RECORD

CULTURE: Influences of Canaanite, Syrian, and Aegean | **ERA:** 11ᵗʰ–10ᵗʰ century BC | **FEATURED ELEMENT:** Baal flanked by two sphinxes

IS DAVID RECORDED IN HISTORY?

Critics had long denied the existence of King David, claiming he was a legendary figure akin to King Arthur of British lore. The discovery of the Tel Dan Stele in 1993 vindicated the biblical record.

The inscription is attributed to Hazael, king of Damascus, whose brutal wars against the kingdoms of Israel and Judah in the 9th century BC (about 150 years after David's reign) are recorded in the Bible (2 Kings 10–13). Written in early Aramaic, the text boasts of killing a king of "the house of David" (Aramaic *bytdwd*). "House of David" is used more than twenty times in the Old Testament to refer to the royal descendants of David who ruled the kingdom of Judah for nearly 400 years.

"the house of David"

Tel Dan Stele
Photo by Tim Chaffey

The "house of David" wording may also appear on a damaged portion of the Mesha Stele, which was erected around 840 BC by Moab's King Mesha. A single letter is missing after the word "house" and the next two letters are the last two consonants in David's name. The stone also mentions Israel's God, Yahweh, and the "house of Omri," a king of Israel and founder of Samaria (1 Kings 16:23–28). Later Assyrian texts identify the rulers of Samaria by the phrase "house of Omri."

DID DAVID'S GIANT FOE EXIST?

A small potsherd discovered in 2005 at Tell es-Safi, called Gath in the Bible, lends some archaeological support to the name of David's giant Philistine foe, Goliath. Two names written on the shard are etymologically similar to Goliath. While this inscription does not necessarily mention the famous giant, it reveals that names like his were used in his hometown during David's lifetime.

7 cm

TLW   TWLA
(To be read right to left)

Tell es-Safi Potsherd (enlarged 2 x)
Photo courtesy of Prof. Aren M. Maeir, Director, the Tell es-Safi/Gath Archaeological Project

The illustration above, based on a bowl discovered at Tell-es-Safi, represents the vessel this potsherd may have originally come from.

HEZEKIAH

THE BIBLICAL RECORD

The nation split after Solomon's reign, resulting in a northern kingdom, Israel, and a southern kingdom, Judah. Hezekiah lived three centuries later and was one of Judah's godliest kings. He destroyed the idols and pagan worship sites throughout the land. Loyal to Yahweh, Hezekiah obeyed the commandments that God gave to Moses, and the Lord caused him to prosper in his endeavors (2 Kings 18:6).

During the sixth year of Hezekiah's reign, the Assyrians conquered the northern kingdom of Israel and carried the people away as captives because they repeatedly sinned against Yahweh. Over the next decade, the Assyrian army conquered numerous cities throughout the land before eventually besieging Jerusalem.

YAHWEH VS. THE ASSYRIAN GODS

With the Assyrian army stationed around Jerusalem, the spokesperson for King Sennacherib of Assyria taunted the inhabitants of the city in the Hebrew language. He recounted his nation's military successes and encouraged the people to surrender.

> "Do not let Hezekiah mislead you when he says, 'Yahweh will rescue us.' Has any of the gods of the nations rescued his land from the hand of the king of Assyria? The gods of Hamath and Arpad—where are they? Where are the gods of Sepharvaim? Did any gods rescue Samaria from my hand? Who among all the gods of these lands have rescued their lands from my hand? So will Yahweh deliver Jerusalem from my power?" (Isaiah 36:18–20)

Hezekiah prayed, "O Yahweh our God, I pray that you save us from his hand so that all the kingdoms of the earth may know that you, O Yahweh, alone are God" (2 Kings 19:19).

The angel of the Lord went out at night and killed 185,000 men in the Assyrian camp. His army annihilated, Sennacherib broke camp and returned to Assyria where he was murdered by two of his own sons.

THE ARCHAEOLOGICAL RECORD

CULTURE: Assyrian, Aramean, Cypriot, and Egyptian | **ERA:** 7th–6th century BC | **FEATURED ELEMENT:** Khephri (Egyptian winged scarab)

DID THE ANGEL OF THE LORD GIVE HEZEKIAH VICTORY?

Striking confirmation of the biblical account of Hezekiah's revolt was discovered around 1830 in Nineveh. Known as Sennacherib's Annals, three six-sided clay prisms detail the war records of the Assyrian king who besieged Jerusalem but failed to conquer it.

Taylor Prism
Photo by David Castor

Written in Assyrian cuneiform and dated to 691 BC, the Taylor Prism describes the Assyrian campaign against Hezekiah of Judah. The inscription tells how Hezekiah was trapped in Jerusalem "like a bird in a cage" while the Assyrian king stormed numerous Judean cities and received tribute from the beleaguered king. These details are also included in the biblical account (2 Kings 18:1; Isaiah 36:1).

While the Bible describes Sennacherib's humiliating defeat when the angel of the Lord killed 185,000 Assyrian soldiers in one night (2 Kings 19:35), the Assyrian records unsurprisingly make no mention of this turn of events. Just like dictators in modern times, many ancient rulers only permitted positive information to be written about them. It is rather telling that the Taylor Prism describes the siege of Jerusalem but never claims that Sennacherib took Jerusalem.

HEZEKIAH'S SEAL

1.3 cm

Hezekiah's bulla (enlarged 15x)
Courtesy of Dr. Eilat Mazar, Photo by Ouria Tadmor

In 2009, a stamped clay seal, called a bulla, was found during excavations south of the Temple Mount at Jerusalem. The seal is inscribed with the Hebrew phrase, "Belonging to Hezekiah [son of] Ahaz, king of Judah." In 2018, a bulla bearing the name of Isaiah and the first three letters of the Hebrew word for "prophet"—the last letter in the word is broken off—was discovered just ten feet away from the Hezekiah bulla.

HEZEKIAH'S TUNNEL

According to the Bible, Hezekiah anticipated the Assyrian assault by repairing and expanding the walls of Jerusalem and constructing an underground shaft to safeguard the city's water supply (2 Chronicles 32:2–4). Excavations in Jerusalem have identified the remains of Hezekiah's "Broad Wall" and the famous water shaft known today as Hezekiah's Tunnel.

DANIEL

THE BIBLICAL RECORD

Deported to Babylon as a youth around 605 BC when King Nebuchadnezzar took control of Jerusalem, Daniel and three of his friends distinguished themselves among the young Judean captives. They quickly rose to prominence in the court of Nebuchadnezzar when the Lord gave the king a disturbing dream and provided Daniel both the content and interpretation of the dream.

Many years later, on the night Babylon was conquered by the Persians, Daniel pronounced judgment against Belshazzar and Babylon as he interpreted the writing that was miraculously written on the wall during the king's feast. Under the Persian ruler Darius, Daniel spent a night in the lions' den for refusing to refrain from praying to the God of Israel as he had always done.

Throughout his remarkable career, Daniel received numerous precise prophecies about the Messiah and the empires that would dominate the ancient Near East.

YAHWEH VS. THE BABYLONIAN GODS

Daniel (Belteshazzar) and his three friends, Hananiah (Shadrach), Mishael (Meshach), and Azariah (Abed-Nego), were given new Babylonian names, each containing an allusion to pagan deities.

Shadrach, Meshach, and Abed-Nego were thrown into the fiery furnace for refusing to worship Nebuchadnezzar's gods and his golden image. When Nebuchadnezzar discovered that God had rescued the men, he wrote a decree that prohibited anyone from speaking against the God of Israel and stated, "No other god exists who is able to rescue in this way" (Daniel 3:29).

Later, the Lord humbled Nebuchadnezzar, causing him to live like an animal for seven years. Afterward, the king proclaimed that Daniel's God was the Most High and that His dominion is everlasting.

Yahweh announced that one way He demonstrates His superiority over the other gods is by accurately telling the future and then bringing it to pass (Isaiah 41:21–29). The many detailed and accurate prophecies revealed to Daniel show God's authority over all other gods.

THE ARCHAEOLOGICAL RECORD

CULTURE: Assyrian and Babylonian | **ERA:** 6ᵗʰ century BC | **FEATURED ELEMENT:** Babylonian sages and demigods called *apkallus*

ARE DANIEL'S PROPHECIES TRUE?

The book of Daniel prophesies the rise and fall of several ancient kingdoms beginning with the Babylonian Empire. These predictions include references to the military conquests of Alexander the Great (Daniel 8:3–8, 20–21), the might of Rome (Daniel 2:40, 7:7), and

the coming of the Messiah and His death (Daniel 9:25–26).

Some modern scholars dismiss the prophetic nature of Daniel, arguing that the book was written 400 years later than Daniel's lifetime. They view the prophecies as being nothing more than a history of events that had already occurred. Is there any evidence that Daniel prophesied future events?

Alexander the Great
Battle of Issus mosaic
Artist Unknown, ca. 100 BC
Photo by Berthold Werner/CC BY-SA 3.0

THE DEAD SEA SCROLLS

Twenty-two fragments from eight manuscripts of the book of Daniel have been recovered among the Dead Sea Scrolls. The fragment known as *4QFlorilegium* confidently recognized Daniel as a prophet. The earliest surviving manuscript (*4QDanᶜ*) dates no later than 125 BC,

and like other Dead Sea Scrolls, it is a copy of an older manuscript. To produce, distribute, and accept these manuscripts as authoritative within the Jewish faith by the mid-second century BC requires that the original composition of Daniel must have been written in the preceding century or earlier.

In fact, the book's internal evidence, such as the Hebrew and Aramaic syntax, vocabulary, spelling, and word order is similar to other ancient texts from the 6th–4th centuries BC. This matches the biblical claim that the book was written in the region of Babylon (Daniel 2:48) and Susa (Daniel 8:2) before 530 BC.

The Dead Sea Scrolls were found in caves near Qumran, Israel. Pictured in the foreground is Cave 4Q.

More importantly, the Lord Jesus Christ referred to Daniel as a prophet and referred to the "abomination of desolation" (Daniel 11:31, 12:11; Matthew 24:15). In identifying Himself as the Messiah and the Son of God, Jesus referenced Daniel's vision of God's throne room and claimed to be the divine "Son of Man" who was given eternal dominion and glory (Daniel 7:10–14; Mark 14:62).

JESUS

THE BIBLICAL RECORD

Jesus of Nazareth is the central figure in the Bible. The New Testament teaches that He is the Son of God, fully God and fully man, who came to earth as the Messiah promised to Israel in the Hebrew Scriptures. Instead of conquering Israel's enemies, as most Jews expected, Jesus led a sinless life, and just as prophesied by Isaiah and Daniel, He died as a sacrifice for our sins. Three days later, He rose from the dead, demonstrating His power over death. After appearing to over 500 people during the next 40 days, Jesus ascended into heaven. Someday He will return to earth to reward those who have believed in Him and to judge the wicked.

DID JESUS EVEN EXIST?

Despite the irrefutable fact that He is the most influential person in history, a growing movement of skeptics claims Jesus never existed. Known as the Christ Myth, this view proposes that early Christians invented the person of Jesus.

These skeptics argue that Scripture is not a valid source to answer the question because the biblical writers were biased. Such a claim displays the skeptic's own bias and their naiveté about the Bible and the use of sources. If we cannot trust the writings of a biased author, then we cannot trust any writing because everyone is biased, including writers who promote the Christ Myth.

Christ "mythicists" go far beyond denying the miraculous; they reject all biblical information about Jesus. This means they are refusing every detail about Jesus from at least eight New Testament sources, most of whom claimed to have known Jesus. Furthermore, nine ancient non-Christian sources refer to Jesus. Ironically, "mythicists" have struggled to identify a single first-century writer who should have written about Jesus but did not.

We can have absolute confidence that Jesus existed because God's Word states that He did.

The Crucifixion of Jesus Christ
To learn more about the life and ministry of Jesus, visit the *Christ, Cross, Consummation* exhibit

JESUS

CULTURE: Hellenistic and Herodian | **ERA:** 1st century AD | **FEATURED ELEMENT:** Replicas of weapons

THE SON OF GOD VS. THE GOD OF THIS WORLD

The Bible explains that when people sacrificed to their gods in the form of idols, they worshiped evil spirits called demons (1 Corinthians 10:19–21; Deuteronomy 32:17).

During His ministry, the Lord Jesus Christ showed His authority over pagan gods. He resisted Satan's temptations and frequently ordered demons to leave the individuals they possessed.

By dying for our sins on the Cross and rising again, He triumphed over these evil spiritual beings of the heavenly realm, exposing them to open shame (Ephesians 6:12; Colossians 2:15–16). In fact, one reason Jesus came into the world was to destroy the works of the devil (1 John 3:8).

WAS JESUS COPIED FROM PAGAN GODS?

Over the past few decades, certain skeptics have claimed that many of the important details about Jesus in the Bible were plagiarized from stories about pagan gods, such as Horus, Mithras, or Zoroaster. For example, a film called *Zeitgeist* claimed that the following ideas were originally written about Horus, long before Jesus was born:

CLAIM ABOUT HORUS	TRUE OR FALSE?
Born on December 25th	Fabricated and Irrelevant*
Mother was a virgin named Isis Meri	Fabricated
Birth marked by a star in the east	Fabricated
Adored by three kings	Fabricated and Irrelevant*
Teacher by age 12	Fabricated
Called the "Lamb of God" and the "Good Shepherd"	Fabricated
Started his ministry at age 30 with 12 disciples	Fabricated
Crucified and buried for three days before rising again	Fabricated

*These claims are irrelevant because the Bible does not teach these ideas about Jesus.

No ancient record about Horus includes these details. The same is true for all the other gods and so-called saviors mentioned by skeptics. Major differences with Jesus are ignored, and perceived similarities are overexaggerated and often arose only after Christianity spread to a region.

Rather than being copied from pagan gods, Jesus demonstrated that He has authority over all gods.

DID JESUS RISE FROM THE DEAD?

ALTERNATIVE SCENARIOS

Skeptics and liberal theologians have proposed numerous theories to account for the compelling evidence of the Resurrection, which is generally acknowledged by a vast majority of scholars in relevant fields, such as history, archaeology, and New Testament studies.

SEEING THINGS

One or more disciples simply had a vivid dream or vision of Jesus and mistook it for an actual encounter. A more popular view claims that the disciples endured grief-induced hallucinations of the risen Savior.

These views cannot explain the empty tomb, or Christ's multiple appearances to groups of people or to unbelievers, such as James and Paul.

BODY EATEN BY ANIMALS

This argument from silence claims that the body was simply discarded in a mass grave with other common criminals where it decomposed and was eaten by scavengers.

Roman law allowed for crucified victims to be buried by loved ones, and Jewish law required it. The Gospels are four early and perfectly reliable sources that report Jesus was buried in Joseph's tomb.

FAKED DEATH

The swoon theory claims that Jesus slipped into a coma-like state on the Cross, recovered in the tomb, and then escaped and appeared to His disciples.

This view misunderstands the brutality of Crucifixion, mocks the efficiency of Roman executioners, rejects modern medical studies concluding that Jesus certainly died on the Cross, and denies the clear biblical descriptions of Christ's death.

DISCIPLES STOLE THE BODY

Jewish authorities claimed that Christ's disciples stole the body while the Roman soldiers slept.

Despite the extreme unlikelihood of Roman soldiers either sleeping on the job or being overpowered by a group of distraught fishermen, this view requires its primary eyewitnesses to have been asleep at the time of the alleged theft.

DID JESUS RISE FROM THE DEAD?

THE ARCHAEOLOGICAL RECORD

THE CRUCIFIXION OF JEHOHANAN

Jehohanan heel bone
with crucifixion spike
Photo by Tim Chaffey

In 1968, a crucifixion spike lodged in a heel bone was discovered in a first-century ossuary inscribed with the name Jehohanan. This find is consistent with the Bible's description of nails being used to crucify Jesus (John 20:25), and contrary to claims of many modern skeptics, it confirmed that crucifixion victims could receive an honorable burial. All four Gospels report that Jesus was buried in the new tomb of Joseph of Arimathea. The biblical and archaeological data matches Jewish burial law (Deuteronomy 21:22–23), Jewish practice (Josephus, *Jewish War*, 48.317), and the Roman law that permitted condemned criminals to be buried by loved ones (*Digesta* 48.24.1.3).

AN IMPERIAL DECREE

The Nazareth Inscription
Photo by Zev Radovan

A marble tablet known as the Nazareth Inscription summarizes a decree written in the AD 40s, in which the Emperor Claudius singled out Israel and prescribed the death penalty for anyone caught stealing a body from a tomb. Grave robbers did not steal bodies; they stole the valuables buried with them. Thus, this decree provides corroborating evidence that the message of Christ's Resurrection had created significant controversy in the Roman Empire within just 15 years of the event, challenging skeptical ideas that the Resurrection was the result of legendary embellishment over several decades.

For more details on the Nazareth Inscription, the evidence for Christ's Resurrection, and the alternative scenarios raised by skeptics, see Tim Chaffey, *In Defense of Easter: Answering Critical Challenges to the Resurrection of Jesus* (Richmond, KY: Risen Books, 2014), available in the bookstore.

DID JESUS RISE FROM THE DEAD?

THE FACTS

The Old Testament prophesied that the Messiah would die and rise from the dead (Psalm 16:10; Isaiah 53:8–12), and the New Testament records the fulfillment of these divine promises. Jesus even pointed to His Resurrection as the sign He would give to the wicked (Matthew 12:39).

INFALLIBLE PROOFS

Jesus appeared multiple times over 40 days to individuals and groups of people (Acts 1:3). To prove He was not a ghost or spirit, He ate, drank, walked, and talked with the people who saw Him.

EXISTENCE OF THE CHURCH

If Jesus did not rise from the dead, Jerusalem would have been the last place for Christianity to get its start since no one would believe the apostles' message. Yet less than two months after the Crucifixion, thousands of Jews came to faith in Jesus as their Messiah.

CHANGE IN THE DISCIPLES

On the night Jesus was arrested, His disciples fled in fear. Yet seven weeks later and even though they faced persecution and death, the disciples boldly proclaimed that Jesus was the Messiah and that He had risen from the dead.

CONVERSION OF JAMES

James was the son of Joseph and Mary, a half-brother of Jesus. James did not believe in Jesus prior to the Crucifixion, but that all changed after the Resurrection. James saw the risen Lord, and he soon became a leader in the early church.

CONVERSION OF PAUL

The church's greatest persecutor met the risen Savior on the road to Damascus one day (Acts 9:3–6). This man who had executed Christians became a great evangelist, planting churches all over the Roman Empire and writing 13 New Testament books.

EMPTY TOMB

Although guarded by Roman soldiers, the tomb in which Jesus had been buried was found empty on the third day. Even those who opposed Jesus and His message admitted this fact (Matthew 28:11–15).

HE IS RISEN

Although they have tried for nearly 2,000 years, skeptics have been unable to produce a single viable theory that refutes the Bible's claim that God raised Jesus from the dead. Some views, such as the swoon theory and the disciples stealing the body, require a group of men to give their lives proclaiming a message they knew to be a lie. Furthermore, none of their theories can even account for just two pieces of evidence: the empty tomb and the post-Resurrection appearances.

ACTS: GOD'S WORD

"...YOU WILL BE MY WITNESSES IN JERUSALEM, AND IN ALL JUDEA AND SAMARIA, AND TO THE ENDS OF THE EARTH." **(ACTS 1:8)**

THE BIBLICAL RECORD

The book of Acts describes how God's message, largely restricted to Israel for centuries, quickly filled the Roman Empire in the mid-first century AD. Jesus told His disciples that they would be His witnesses in Jerusalem, Judea, Samaria, and to the ends of the earth (Acts 1:8). The gospel message started in Jerusalem, and through faithful men like Peter, John, and Paul, it spread throughout the empire, reaching even Rome itself.

YAHWEH VS THE GREEK AND ROMAN GODS

As the Apostle Paul brought the gospel to new cities, he often encountered stiff opposition from followers of pagan gods. After healing a lame man in Lystra, Paul and Barnabas were thought to be Hermes and Zeus, and the people sought to offer sacrifices to them. Paul used the opportunity to teach them about the God who made all things, but the crowd reacted by stoning him and leaving him for dead (Acts 14:15–19).

While speaking about Jesus and the Resurrection in Athens, Paul was accused by certain philosophers of preaching about strange gods. When Paul addressed them in the Areopagus, he spoke of their idols, particularly about their altar "to the unknown god" (Acts 17:23). He told them that their unknown god was the Creator, and He could not be contained by manmade temples and idols because He is the Lord of heaven and earth.

In Philippi, Paul cast a demon out of a servant girl who made her owners a lot of money through fortune-telling. He and Silas were beaten and thrown in prison, but God freed them via an earthquake, and the jailor trusted in Christ (Acts 16:16–34).

In Ephesus, home to the famous Temple of Artemis (Diana), Paul performed many miraculous deeds while teaching the word of the Lord. The Ephesian economy was drastically impacted as the people burned their books on magic and stopped purchasing idols of Artemis. The city's craftsmen feared that their major source of revenue would dry up since so many people had converted to the Christian faith (Acts 19:11–41).

REACHES THE WORLD

THE ARCHAEOLOGICAL RECORD

Historical and archaeological discoveries have vindicated Luke, the author of Acts, as an exceptional historian who had clearly visited the places described in the book. For example, he accurately described geographical settings, cited specific land and sea routes, used proper titles for civic leaders in various places, and mentioned distinct customs in many locales.

Ruins of the Temple of Apollo in Corinth

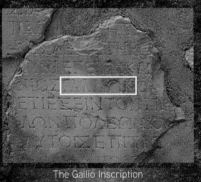

The Gallio Inscription
Photo by Gérard Janot/CC BY-SA 4.0

Excavations in Lystra unearthed a first-century temple and multiple inscriptions citing Zeus and Hermes as the city's most important gods, along with expectations that they would return to earth. This matches Luke's description of the people's reaction to Paul and Barnabas in Acts 14.

In Corinth, some Jews brought Paul before Gallio, the proconsul of Achaia. Digs at Corinth have uncovered the judgment seat where this event took place, known in Greek as the *bema* (Acts 18:12–17). In 1905, archaeologists discovered a stone slab in Delphi, a city of ancient Achaia, bearing an inscription dated to AD 51–53 identifying Gallio as the proconsul of that region.

Several finds from Ephesus corroborate the biblical account in Acts 19. Paul taught in the school of Tyrannus for two years (v. 9). A stone pillar from the first century AD bearing the name of Tyrannus has been found among the ruins. The large theater used by the rioters against Paul (v. 29) has been unearthed. The remains of the Temple of Artemis (v. 27) and an idol of Artemis (v. 26) have also been uncovered. The title of the region's high-ranking officials, *Asiarchs* (v. 31), was discovered on a pillar in Miletus, 30 miles south of Ephesus.

The Great Theater of Ephesus

ACTS: GOD'S WORD REACHES THE WORLD

THE HISTORICAL RECORD

Many ancient historians wrote about Jesus and His earliest followers, and even though they were not Christians, the information they provide matches the details revealed in the Gospels and Acts.

Pliny the Younger (AD 61–112)
Roman author and governor of Bithynia and Asia Minor

"[The Christians] were in the habit of meeting on a certain fixed day before it was light, when they sang in alternate verses a hymn to Christ, as to a god..." *(Letters 2.10:96)*

Cornelius Tacitus (AD 55–120)
Greatest historian of ancient Rome

"Consequently, to get rid of the report [that he had burned Rome], Nero fastened the guilt and inflicted the most exquisite tortures on a class hated for their abominations, called Christians by the populace. Christus, from whom the name had its origin, suffered the extreme penalty during the reign of Tiberius at the hands of one of our procurators, Pontius Pilatus, and a most mischievous superstition, thus checked for the moment, again broke out not only in Judaea, the first source of the evil, but even in Rome..." *(Annals 15.44)*

Suetonius (AD 69–130)
Chief secretary of Emperor Hadrian with access to imperial records

"Because the Jews at Rome caused continuous disturbances at the instigation of Chrestus, he expelled them from the city. After the great fire at Rome...punishments were also inflicted on the Christians, a sect professing a new and mischievous religious belief." *(Claudius, 25)*

* "Chrestus" is a variant of the Latin word for Christ.

Lucian (AD 2nd century)
Greek satirist who mocked Christians

"The Christians, you know, worship a man to this day—the distinguished personage who introduced their novel rites, and was crucified on that account....You see, these misguided creatures start with the general conviction that they are immortal for all time...and deny the gods of Greece, and worship the crucified sage, and live after his laws." *(The Death of Peregrine, 11–13, in H.W. Fowler and F.G. Fowler, trans., The Works of Lucian of Samosata, 1905)*

ACTS: THE JOURNEYS OF THE APOSTLES

TO JUDEA AND SAMARIA
c. AD 33–44

Acts 1–12 highlights the growth of the church in Jerusalem, Judea, and Samaria after Jesus ascended into heaven. Peter and John feature prominently in these chapters as the early Christians faced intense persecution for proclaiming that Jesus of Nazareth was the crucified and risen Jewish Messiah (2:22–26) and the only way by which a person could be saved (4:12).

▸ *Acts 1–5: the number of believers grows in Jerusalem to over 5,000 men despite imprisonment and beatings.*

▸ *Acts 6–7: Stephen is martyred in Jerusalem as persecution intensifies and drives believers throughout Judea and Samaria.*

▸ *Acts 8: Philip preaches in Samaria and to the Ethiopian eunuch.*

▸ *Acts 9: Paul, the church's greatest persecutor, encounters the risen Jesus while on the road to Damascus and converts to the Christian faith. He then flees to Tarsus. Peter preaches in Lydda and Joppa.*

▸ *Acts 10: Gentiles are converted when Peter proclaims the gospel to Cornelius and his household in Caesarea.*

▸ *Acts 12: King Herod Agrippa executes James, the brother of John, and imprisons Peter. An angel frees Peter, and Herod dies for refusing to glorify God.*

PHILIP'S TRAVELS
PETER'S TRAVELS
PAUL TO DAMASCUS (CONVERSION)
PAUL AND BARNABAS (ANTIOCH)

Map © AWMC © KlokanTech © DARE © Mapbox © OpenStreetMap
Additional data © Copyright 2018 Robert Rouse

ACTS: THE JOURNEYS OF THE APOSTLES

TO THE ENDS OF THE EARTH

c. AD 44–62

Acts 13–38 traces the development of the church as it spread throughout the Roman Empire. While a few chapters take place in Jerusalem, most of the material is based on Paul's numerous missionary journeys that saw him planting churches in Asia Minor and Greece. The book ends with Paul under house arrest in Rome. Based largely on details from Paul's later epistles, many biblical scholars believe Paul was eventually set free and made at least one more missionary journey before being arrested and executed under the Roman Emperor Nero around AD 67.

› *Acts 13–14:* **Paul's First Missionary Journey**–*Paul and Barnabas preach the gospel on Cyprus and in cities in Pamphylia, Galatia, and Cilicia.*

› *Acts 15:1–29: The apostles meet in Jerusalem and reject the notion that Gentile believers in Jesus Christ must be circumcised and follow the Law of Moses.*

› *Acts 15:30–18:21:* **Paul's Second Missionary Journey**—*After splitting with Barnabas, who traveled with Mark to Cyprus, Paul and Silas traveled through Asia Minor and Greece to plant churches.*

› *Acts 18:22–21:17:* **Paul's Third Missionary Journey**—*Paul and Silas visit many of the churches planted during their previous journey, encouraging them to remain faithful.*

› *Acts 21:18–28:31: Following the arrest in Jerusalem and two-year imprisonment in Caesarea, Paul is taken to Rome and placed under house arrest. This journey is sometimes referred to as* **Paul's Fourth Missionary Journey.**

"AND YOU WILL BE MY WITNESSES IN JERUSALEM, AND IN ALL JUDEA AND SAMARIA, AND TO THE ENDS OF THE EARTH." (ACTS 1:8)

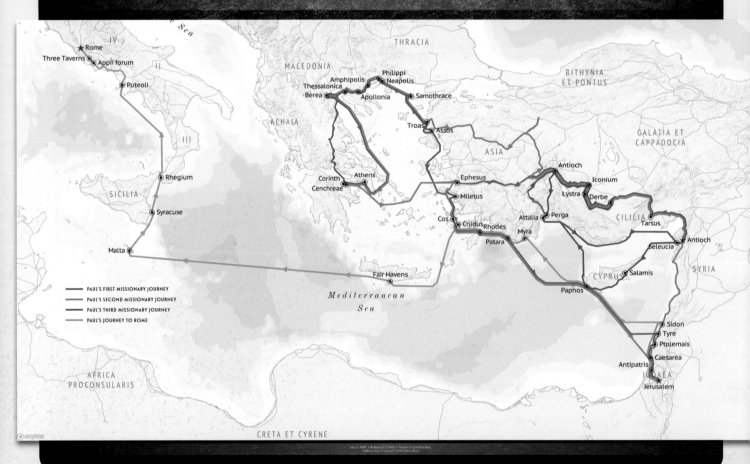

PAUL'S FIRST MISSIONARY JOURNEY
PAUL'S SECOND MISSIONARY JOURNEY
PAUL'S THIRD MISSIONARY JOURNEY
PAUL'S JOURNEY TO ROME

THE MOST **UNIQUE BOOK** IN THE WORLD

TRANSMISSION AND PRESERVATION OF THE TEXT

Illustration of a scribe from a facsimile of William Tyndale's 1525 edition of the English New Testament. From the Reed Rare Books Collection in Dunedin, New Zealand.

The biblical books were originally written on papyrus or parchment and some portions were even carved into stone tablets. Papyrus sheets are formed by combining two layers of split papyrus reeds, and parchments are made from sheepskin or goatskin. Scrolls were formed by joining the edges of multiple papyri or parchments.

Throughout much of ancient Israel's history, Old Testament scrolls were kept in the temple. As synagogues sprang up in the centuries before the birth of Christ, copies of scrolls were made for these assembly places.

The New Testament writings were originally penned on scrolls and sent to individuals (e.g., Timothy, Theophilus), individual churches (e.g., Corinth, Thessalonica), or groups of churches in a region (e.g., Galatians). Copies were soon made by scribes to be distributed to churches throughout the Roman Empire and beyond.

As early as the second century AD, most of the books had reached a number of churches, and Christians frequently compiled their writings into an early form of the book, known as a codex. This innovation allowed believers to carry a large amount of Scripture in a compact format, and it also elevated the need to identify which writings were authoritative and inspired by the Holy Spirit.

Since that time, the Bible has been copied, translated, sold, and read more than any other book in history.

THE MOST UNIQUE BOOK

OLD TESTAMENT BOOKS

GENESIS	EXODUS	LEVITICUS	NUMBERS	DEUTERONOMY	JOSHUA	JUDGES
AUTHOR MOSES	AUTHOR MOSES	AUTHOR MOSES	AUTHOR MOSES	AUTHOR MOSES	AUTHOR JOSHUA	AUTHOR UNKNOWN

RUTH	1 SAMUEL	2 SAMUEL	1 KINGS	2 KINGS	1 CHRONICLES	2 CHRONICLES
AUTHOR UNKNOWN	AUTHOR UNKNOWN	AUTHOR UNKNOWN	AUTHOR UNKNOWN	AUTHOR UNKNOWN	AUTHOR EZRA	AUTHOR EZRA

EZRA	NEHEMIAH	ESTHER
AUTHOR EZRA	AUTHOR NEHEMIAH	AUTHOR UNKNOWN

JOB	PSALMS	PROVERBS	ECCLESIASTES	SONG OF SONGS
AUTHOR UNKNOWN	AUTHOR DAVID / VARIOUS	AUTHOR SOLOMON / AGUR / LEMUEL	AUTHOR SOLOMON	AUTHOR SOLOMON

ISAIAH	JEREMIAH	LAMENTATIONS	EZEKIEL	DANIEL	HOSEA	JOEL
AUTHOR ISAIAH	AUTHOR JEREMIAH	AUTHOR JEREMIAH	AUTHOR EZEKIEL	AUTHOR DANIEL	AUTHOR HOSEA	AUTHOR JOEL

AMOS	OBADIAH	JONAH	MICAH	NAHUM	HABAKKUK	ZEPHANIAH
AUTHOR AMOS	AUTHOR OBADIAH	AUTHOR JONAH	AUTHOR MICAH	AUTHOR NAHUM	AUTHOR HABAKKUK	AUTHOR ZEPHANIAH

HAGGAI	ZECHARIAH	MALACHI
AUTHOR HAGGAI	AUTHOR ZECHARIAH	AUTHOR MALACHI

IN THE WORLD

THE BIBLE IS A COLLECTION OF 66 BOOKS WRITTEN OVER A 1,500-YEAR PERIOD BY APPROXIMATELY 40 DIFFERENT AUTHORS USING MULTIPLE GENRES FROM 3 CONTINENTS IN 3 LANGUAGES WHILE MAINTAINING 1 CONSISTENT MESSAGE.

NEW TESTAMENT BOOKS

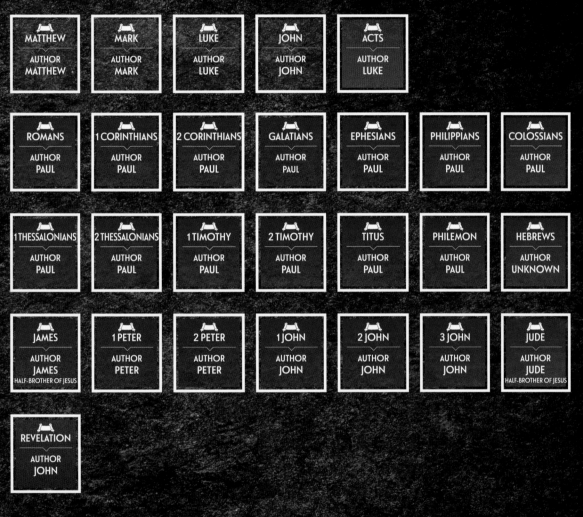

MATTHEW	MARK	LUKE	JOHN	ACTS
AUTHOR MATTHEW	AUTHOR MARK	AUTHOR LUKE	AUTHOR JOHN	AUTHOR LUKE

ROMANS	1 CORINTHIANS	2 CORINTHIANS	GALATIANS	EPHESIANS	PHILIPPIANS	COLOSSIANS
AUTHOR PAUL	AUTHOR PAUL	AUTHOR PAUL	AUTHOR PAUL	AUTHOR PAUL	AUTHOR PAUL	AUTHOR PAUL

1 THESSALONIANS	2 THESSALONIANS	1 TIMOTHY	2 TIMOTHY	TITUS	PHILEMON	HEBREWS
AUTHOR PAUL	AUTHOR PAUL	AUTHOR PAUL	AUTHOR PAUL	AUTHOR PAUL	AUTHOR PAUL	AUTHOR UNKNOWN

JAMES	1 PETER	2 PETER	1 JOHN	2 JOHN	3 JOHN	JUDE
AUTHOR JAMES HALF-BROTHER OF JESUS	AUTHOR PETER	AUTHOR PETER	AUTHOR JOHN	AUTHOR JOHN	AUTHOR JOHN	AUTHOR JUDE HALF-BROTHER OF JESUS

REVELATION
AUTHOR JOHN

HISTORY   WISDOM/ POETRY   PROPHETIC   BIOGRAPHY   LETTER

Traditional authorship is assumed for this chart. This view recognizes that the authors often employed scribes to write for them. For example, Jeremiah instructed Baruch to pen his words (Jeremiah 36:32), and Tertius wrote Romans for Paul (cf. Romans 1:1 and 16:22).

THE BIBLICAL CANON

RECOGNIZING THE CANON

The collection of books in the Bible is referred to as the canon, from the Latin word for rule or standard. The 39 books of the Old Testament were largely agreed upon by the first century AD.

Circumstances in the second century AD necessitated the recognition of the New Testament canon to affirm which writings were authoritative and inspired by the Holy Spirit. The apostles and those who learned directly from them had died, and erroneous books were being written by people using names of key biblical figures.

Except for a handful of books (Hebrews, 2 Peter, 2 and 3 John, Jude, and Revelation), there was practically unanimous acceptance of the New Testament writings as Scripture during the second century AD, and even the disputed books were accepted by most churches. In AD 367 Athanasius listed the 27 books of the New Testament as the complete canon, and the church councils at Hippo Regius (AD 393) and Carthage (AD 397) affirmed his list.

THE NEW TESTAMENT BOOKS MET CERTAIN CRITERIA.[1]

Was the book written by an apostle or his close associate?

Was the writer confirmed by acts of God?

Did the message tell the truth about God?

Does it come with the power of God?

Was it accepted by the people of God?

Ultimately, God determined which books belong in the Bible, and the Holy Spirit inspired the writing of these books to teach and guide His people. The church does not determine the canon. Instead, believers indwelt by the Holy Spirit can recognize His voice (John 10:2–5) and discover which books were inspired by Him.

[1] Norman L. Geisler and William E. Nix, *A General Introduction to the Bible, Revised and Expanded* (Chicago, IL: Moody Publishers, 1986), pp. 229–231.

THE BIBLICAL CANON

CULTURE: Greek and Roman | ERA: 1st century AD | FEATURED ELEMENT: Greek gods Atlas and Athena

SHOULD THE APOCRYPHA BE INCLUDED?

A compilation of books known as the Apocrypha has been the focus of countless debates on the canon. Written during the "Intertestamental Period" (the four centuries between Malachi and Matthew), the following books have been accepted by some traditions and rejected by others:

1 and 2 Esdras	Baruch (including the Letter of Jeremiah)
Tobit	Additions to Daniel
Judith	‣ Song of the Three Youths (3:24–90)
Additions to Esther (10:4–16:24)	‣ Susanna (13:1–65)
Wisdom of Solomon	‣ Bel and the Dragon (14:1–42)
Ecclesiasticus (Sirach)	1 and 2 Maccabees

EASTERN ORTHODOX - Eastern Orthodox churches have long accepted the Apocrypha in their canon because these writings were included in early editions of the Septuagint, the Greek translation of the Hebrew Scriptures frequently used by the earliest Christians.

ROMAN CATHOLIC - In response to the Protestant Reformation's criticism of certain doctrines, such as prayers for the dead and Purgatory, the Roman Catholic Church, which had always held the Apocrypha in high regard, officially canonized the Apocrypha in 1546 at the Council of Trent.

PROTESTANT - Most Protestants reject the inspiration and canonicity of these writings, although the books are generally considered useful for background studies.

PROTESTANTS CITE THE FOLLOWING REASONS TO EXCLUDE THE APOCRYPHA FROM THE CANON

The books contain teachings contrary to the rest of Scripture

‣ *Prayers for the dead (2 Maccabees 12:39–46)*

‣ *Giving of alms brings forgiveness of sins (Tobit 12:9)*

The New Testament never quotes the Apocrypha as authoritative

‣ *Hebrews 11:35–38 likely alludes to the martyrs in 2 Maccabees 6–7. This acknowledgement of the events cannot be viewed as an endorsement of divine inspiration since biblical writers frequently cited historical events not mentioned in Scripture and even quoted pagan poets.*

The books never claim to speak for the Lord

‣ *1 Maccabees 9:27 practically denies inspiration by stating prophets were not in the land at the time.*

THE BIBLICAL CANON

MYTHS ABOUT THE CANON

Misunderstandings about the canonization process abound. Some are promoted by well-intentioned believers relying on outdated ideas while others, based on fabrications and revisionist history, are advanced by skeptics determined to undermine biblical authority.

"COUNCIL" OF JAMNIA

In 1871, a German scholar speculated that Jewish rabbis and scholars gathered at Jamnia (Yavneh) in AD 90 to officially determine which books belonged in the Hebrew Scriptures. Many Christians have since referred to this hypothetical council as one of the arguments against including the Apocrypha in the canon. However, there is little evidence for such an event.

Meetings were often held in Jamnia between AD 70–132, but none of these could accurately be considered an authoritative council. The early rabbinic sources refer to the gatherings as a house of study or an academy. One meeting included a discussion about Ecclesiastes and the Song of Solomon, but no formal decision was reached. Furthermore, there is no evidence of discussion about the Apocrypha.

THE COUNCIL OF NICAEA BANNED BOOKS

Largely due to misinformation peddled in popular novels like *The Da Vinci Code* and documentaries like the History Channel's *Banned from the Bible*, many people believe that scores of early books strongly vied for inclusion in the canon but were ultimately rejected by power-hungry church leaders at the Council of Nicaea in AD 325.

First Council of Nicaea, 16th century Byzantine icon

The truth is that the canon was not on the agenda at Nicaea, and hardly any of these writings were ever given any consideration for the canon at any point. Many are outright heretical, having Gnostic origins in the second or third centuries—long after the death of the apostles. Others are obvious forgeries, known as pseudepigrapha, and one book mentioned by the History Channel may well be a fraud dating to the 1950s.

HOW DOES THE MANUSCRIPT EVIDENCE FOR THE **NEW TESTAMENT** STACK UP AGAINST **OTHER ANCIENT WORKS?**

ILIAD
AUTHOR: HOMER
DATE: ca. 800 BC
EARLIEST MS: ca. 400 BC
TIME GAP: 400 YRS

1,757

HISTORY OF ROME
AUTHOR: LIVY
DATE: 27 BC–AD 17
EARLIEST MS: EARLY 5TH C.
TIME GAP: 400 YRS

150

NEW TESTAMENT
AUTHOR: MANY AUTHORS
DATE: ca. AD 50–95
EARLIEST MS: AD 130
TIME GAP: 40 YRS

5,795

HISTORY
AUTHOR: THUCYDIDES
DATE: 431–400 BC
EARLIEST MS: 3RD C. BC
TIME GAP: 200 YRS

96

NATURAL HISTORY
AUTHOR: PLINY THE ELDER
DATE: AD 49–79
EARLIEST MS: 5TH C.
TIME GAP: 400 YRS

200

● icon represents **50 MANUSCRIPTS AND FRAGMENTS**

THE SUPREME AUTHORITY IN HEAVEN AND ON EARTH

CULTURE: Roman | **ERA:** 1st century AD | **FEATURED ELEMENT:** Deified emperor

יהוה
YAHWEH IS LORD OF ALL

The God of the Bible repeatedly demonstrated His authority over the powers in heaven and on earth. Since no one can thwart His plans (Isaiah 43:11–13), and since He cannot lie (Titus 1:2), we can have absolute confidence that His Word is both true and authoritative.

Someday, He will put all His enemies under His feet (1 Corinthians 15:24–28). Every individual who refuses to turn to God will be put down. This includes the spiritual entities behind the false religions of our world and human beings who imagine themselves to be gods or live as if they are their own god.

Illustrated here is a broken statue of Zeus, the leader of the pantheon of Greek gods who supposedly met on Mt. Olympus. Ultimately, no philosophy or power in heaven or on earth will be able to stand against Yahweh.

> FOR THIS REASON GOD HAS HIGHLY EXALTED HIM AND GIVEN HIM THE NAME THAT IS ABOVE EVERY NAME, SO THAT AT THE NAME OF JESUS EVERY KNEE WILL BOW, IN HEAVEN AND ON EARTH AND UNDER THE EARTH, AND EVERY TONGUE WILL CONFESS THAT JESUS CHRIST IS LORD, TO THE GLORY OF GOD THE FATHER.
> (PHILIPPIANS 2:9–11)

THE RELEVANCE OF GENESIS EXHIBIT

This room is themed as a reclaimed warehouse space because it is a building with a strong foundation that has been restored after a period of neglect.

This serves as a metaphor for the modern church since the foundational book of Genesis has been neglected and rejected by some Christians as they attempt to force billions of years into the Bible. The church needs to reclaim Scripture's solid foundation to properly address many of the major problems facing our modern world.

IN SEVERAL PLACES YOU WILL FIND NOTES AND ARTWORK from the character who fixed up this space, as he explains his own journey toward understanding the relevance of Genesis.

AS I REFLECTED ON IMPORTANT CONTROVERSIES IN OUR CULTURE, SUCH AS ABORTION AND MARRIAGE, AND EVEN DEBATE OVER THE MEANING OF RIGHT AND WRONG, I REALIZED THAT THE PROPER FOUNDATION FOR ADDRESSING ALL OF THESE ISSUES IS FOUND IN GENESIS, AND I HAVE NO RIGHT TO CHANGE GODS WORD.

All phrases from Proverbs 8 which personifies Wisdom as a woman

ORIGIN OF

- For example, I oppose abortion and euthanasia because God created all people in His image and He said murder is wrong. Every person has immeasurable value, from the unborn child to the frail grandmother in the nursing home.

- Even though many in our culture seek to redefine marriage, God ordained it at the beginning to be a union of one man and one woman.

Sanctity of Life

Marriage

Justice

Stewardship

Death

בראשית

Hebrew title for book of Genesis

Genesis IS THE Foundation OF Morality Marriage Justice...

DID GOD USE EVOLUTION?

THEISTIC EVOLUTION CONTRADICTS THE TEXT

God made man from the dust of the ground (not from ape-like ancestors), and He made man (not apes) in His image. Also, God created miraculously over six 24-hour days rather than through natural processes over billions of years.

COULD GOD HAVE USED EVOLUTION?

God is holy and loving and tells us that death is an enemy. So how could He create all life using a process like evolution, a philosophy of death that requires the suffering, disease, and death of trillions of creatures for billions of years?

WHICH CAME FIRST?

CREATION
Earth > Sun
Fruit Trees > Land Animals
Birds > Land Reptiles
Whales > Land Mammals

EVOLUTION/BIG BANG
Sun > Earth
Land Animals > Fruit Trees
Land Reptiles > Birds
Land Mammals > Whales

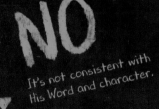

NO

It's not consistent with His Word and character.

83

COULD GOD HAVE USED MILLIONS OF YEARS?

EVERY ATTEMPT TO FIT MILLIONS OF YEARS INTO GENESIS ENDS UP WITH MANY OF THE SAME <u>PROBLEMS.</u>

DAY-AGE THEORY (DAT)
(Progressive creation)
Each day of the creation week lasted for millions of years.

COSMIC TEMPLE (CT)
Genesis I is not about the creation of the physical universe but is about God creating and inaugurating His own cosmic temple, being modeled after pagan temple stories.

THEISTIC EVOLUTION (TE.)
God created everything using evolutionary processes over millions of years.

LITERARY FRAMEWORK (LF)
Genesis I is not historical narrative but a semi-poetic retelling of God's creative work that says nothing about the age of the earth or universe.

HISTORICAL CREATION (HC)
Genesis 1:1 describes God's creation of the universe and earth over millions of years. The remaining verses of Genesis I and 2 are just about the preparation of the land that would become known as Israel.

GAP THEORY (GT)
A gap of millions of years is placed between the first two verses of the Bible.

CREATION WAS NOT "VERY GOOD"
Genesis 1:31

TE, HC, DAT, GT, LF, CT

DEATH + THORNS BEFORE SIN

LF, DAT, HC, CT, GT, TE

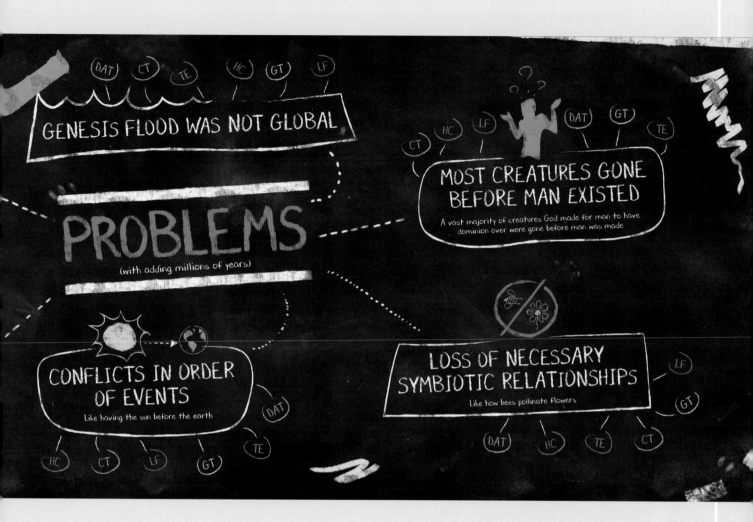

GENESIS FLOOD WAS NOT GLOBAL

DAT CT TE HC GT LF

PROBLEMS

(with adding millions of years)

MOST CREATURES GONE
BEFORE MAN EXISTED

A vast majority of creatures God made for man to have
dominion over were gone before man was made

CT HC LF DAT GT TE

CONFLICTS IN ORDER
OF EVENTS

Like having the sun before the earth

HC CT LF GT DAT TE

LOSS OF NECESSARY
SYMBIOTIC RELATIONSHIPS

Like how bees pollinate flowers

DAT HC TE CT LF GT

A BATTLE OF TWO·VIEWS

These castles represent the ongoing battle between the naturalistic worldview based on man's word and the biblical worldview founded on God's Word.

THE PROBLEM

For the past few centuries, secularists have used their interpretation of origins to assault the foundational book of the Bible—Genesis. Their attacks are largely focused on that rock-solid foundation.

Meanwhile, the church often fails to respond appropriately. Some Christians shoot at fellow believers and others are asleep as the battle rages. Even worse, some even attack their own foundation, the authority of God's Word, when they claim that the Creation and Flood accounts in Genesis are not historically accurate. Thankfully, some Christians fight against the symptoms of humanistic thinking in our culture, such as abortion, pornography, and homosexual behavior, but these efforts will ultimately fall short since naturalism's sandy foundation remains untouched.

THE SOLUTION

This battle is being fought at the foundational level. Christians must reclaim their own foundation—the authority of God's Word beginning in Genesis 1—and stand firm upon it. Rather than compromising with evolutionary ideas, a concerted effort must be made to destroy the foundational beliefs of the opposing worldview—the naturalistic philosophy along with its billions of years and evolution. Without that foundation, the symptoms of naturalistic thinking cannot stand.

The Lord Jesus Christ said that a wise man builds his house on the rock while a foolish man builds his house on the sand. (Matthew 7:24-27)

MAN'S WORD

GOD'S WORD

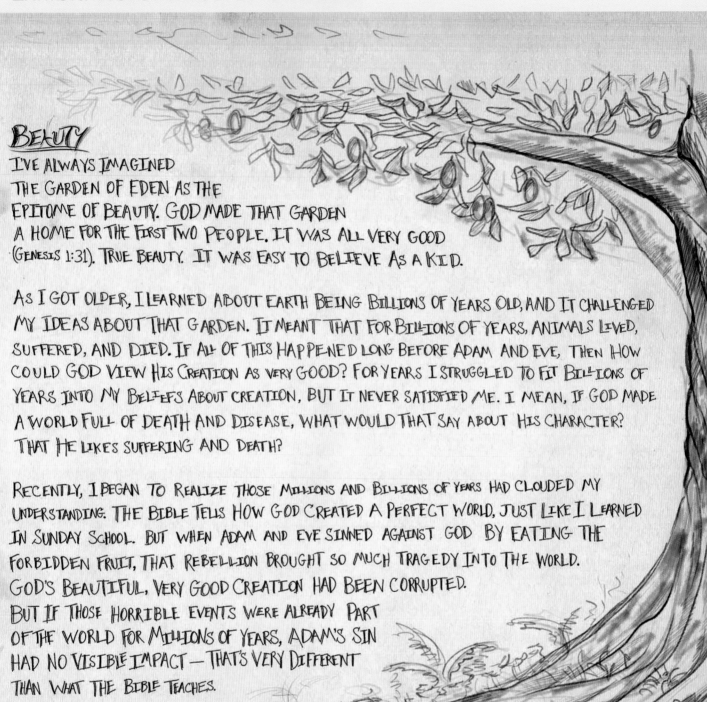

BEAUTY

I'VE ALWAYS IMAGINED
THE GARDEN OF EDEN AS THE
EPITOME OF BEAUTY. GOD MADE THAT GARDEN
A HOME FOR THE FIRST TWO PEOPLE. IT WAS ALL VERY GOOD
(GENESIS 1:31). TRUE BEAUTY. IT WAS EASY TO BELIEVE AS A KID.

AS I GOT OLDER, I LEARNED ABOUT EARTH BEING BILLIONS OF YEARS OLD, AND IT CHALLENGED
MY IDEAS ABOUT THAT GARDEN. IT MEANT THAT FOR BILLIONS OF YEARS, ANIMALS LIVED,
SUFFERED, AND DIED. IF ALL OF THIS HAPPENED LONG BEFORE ADAM AND EVE, THEN HOW
COULD GOD VIEW HIS CREATION AS VERY GOOD? FOR YEARS I STRUGGLED TO FIT BILLIONS OF
YEARS INTO MY BELIEFS ABOUT CREATION, BUT IT NEVER SATISFIED ME. I MEAN, IF GOD MADE
A WORLD FULL OF DEATH AND DISEASE, WHAT WOULD THAT SAY ABOUT HIS CHARACTER?
THAT HE LIKES SUFFERING AND DEATH?

RECENTLY, I BEGAN TO REALIZE THOSE MILLIONS AND BILLIONS OF YEARS HAD CLOUDED MY
UNDERSTANDING. THE BIBLE TELLS HOW GOD CREATED A PERFECT WORLD, JUST LIKE I LEARNED
IN SUNDAY SCHOOL. BUT WHEN ADAM AND EVE SINNED AGAINST GOD BY EATING THE
FORBIDDEN FRUIT, THAT REBELLION BROUGHT SO MUCH TRAGEDY INTO THE WORLD.
GOD'S BEAUTIFUL, VERY GOOD CREATION HAD BEEN CORRUPTED.
BUT IF THOSE HORRIBLE EVENTS WERE ALREADY PART
OF THE WORLD FOR MILLIONS OF YEARS, ADAM'S SIN
HAD NO VISIBLE IMPACT — THAT'S VERY DIFFERENT
THAN WHAT THE BIBLE TEACHES.

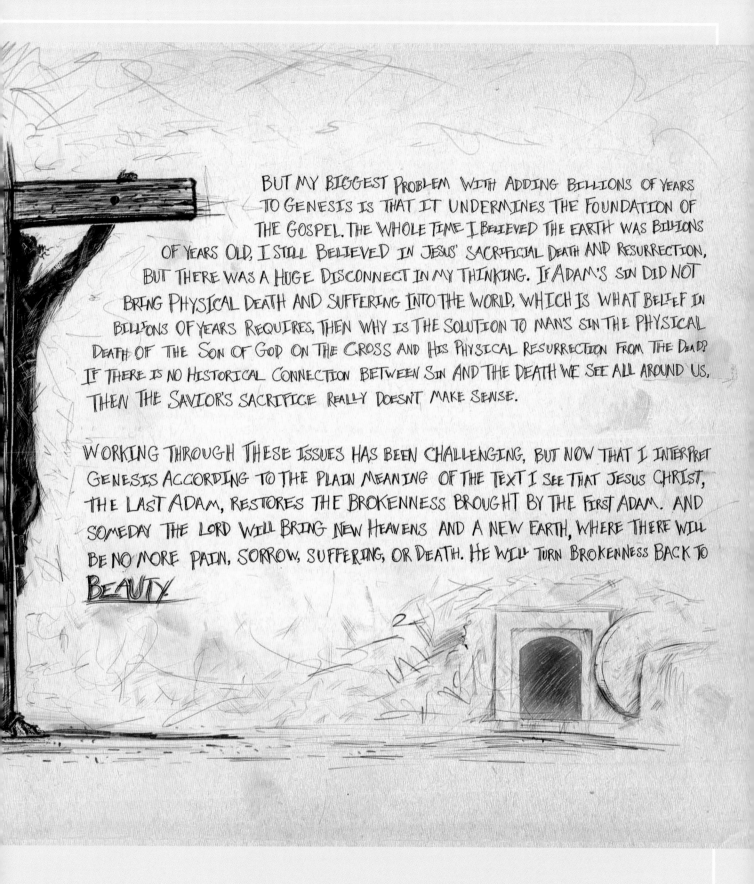

BUT MY BIGGEST PROBLEM WITH ADDING BILLIONS OF YEARS TO GENESIS IS THAT IT UNDERMINES THE FOUNDATION OF THE GOSPEL. THE WHOLE TIME I BELIEVED THE EARTH WAS BILLIONS OF YEARS OLD, I STILL BELIEVED IN JESUS' SACRIFICIAL DEATH AND RESURRECTION, BUT THERE WAS A HUGE DISCONNECT IN MY THINKING. IF ADAM'S SIN DID NOT BRING PHYSICAL DEATH AND SUFFERING INTO THE WORLD, WHICH IS WHAT BELIEF IN BILLIONS OF YEARS REQUIRES, THEN WHY IS THE SOLUTION TO MAN'S SIN THE PHYSICAL DEATH OF THE SON OF GOD ON THE CROSS AND HIS PHYSICAL RESURRECTION FROM THE DEAD? IF THERE IS NO HISTORICAL CONNECTION BETWEEN SIN AND THE DEATH WE SEE ALL AROUND US, THEN THE SAVIOR'S SACRIFICE REALLY DOESN'T MAKE SENSE.

WORKING THROUGH THESE ISSUES HAS BEEN CHALLENGING, BUT NOW THAT I INTERPRET GENESIS ACCORDING TO THE PLAIN MEANING OF THE TEXT I SEE THAT JESUS CHRIST, THE LAST ADAM, RESTORES THE BROKENNESS BROUGHT BY THE FIRST ADAM. AND SOMEDAY THE LORD WILL BRING NEW HEAVENS AND A NEW EARTH, WHERE THERE WILL BE NO MORE PAIN, SORROW, SUFFERING, OR DEATH. HE WILL TURN BROKENNESS BACK TO BEAUTY.

Did Plants Die Before Adam Sinned?

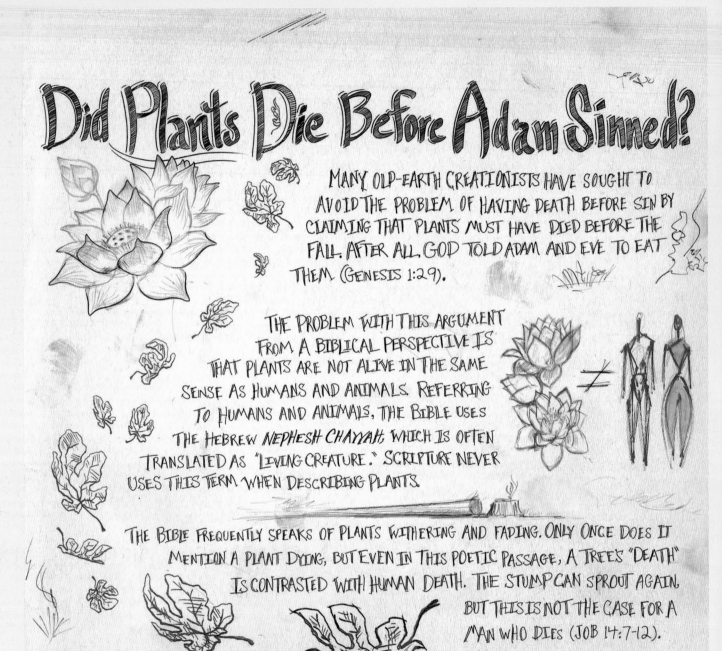

MANY OLD-EARTH CREATIONISTS HAVE SOUGHT TO AVOID THE PROBLEM OF HAVING DEATH BEFORE SIN BY CLAIMING THAT PLANTS MUST HAVE DIED BEFORE THE FALL. AFTER ALL, GOD TOLD ADAM AND EVE TO EAT THEM (GENESIS 1:29).

THE PROBLEM WITH THIS ARGUMENT FROM A BIBLICAL PERSPECTIVE IS THAT PLANTS ARE NOT ALIVE IN THE SAME SENSE AS HUMANS AND ANIMALS. REFERRING TO HUMANS AND ANIMALS, THE BIBLE USES THE HEBREW *NEPHESH CHAYYAH*, WHICH IS OFTEN TRANSLATED AS "LIVING CREATURE." SCRIPTURE NEVER USES THIS TERM WHEN DESCRIBING PLANTS.

THE BIBLE FREQUENTLY SPEAKS OF PLANTS WITHERING AND FADING. ONLY ONCE DOES IT MENTION A PLANT DYING, BUT EVEN IN THIS POETIC PASSAGE, A TREE'S "DEATH" IS CONTRASTED WITH HUMAN DEATH. THE STUMP CAN SPROUT AGAIN, BUT THIS IS NOT THE CASE FOR A MAN WHO DIES (JOB 14:7-12).

DID ANIMALS DIE ⸻ BEFORE ⸻ ADAM SINNED?

OLD-EARTH CREATIONISTS FREQUENTLY ASSERT THAT ADAM'S SIN BROUGHT DEATH TO HUMANS ALONE AND THAT ANIMALS HAD BEEN DYING FOR MILLIONS OF YEARS BEFORE SIN. THEY POINT OUT THAT THE CONTEXT OF THESE <u>VERSES</u> LIMITS DEATH TO HUMANS. IT IS TRUE THAT THESE PASSAGES PRIMARILY ADDRESS HUMAN DEATH, BUT THERE ARE OTHER <u>PASSAGES</u> THAT SHOW ANIMALS DID NOT DIE BEFORE ADAM REBELLED.

"Just as sin came into the world through one man, and death through sin, so death spread to all men because all sinned."
(ROMANS 5:12)

"For as by a man came death, by a man has also come the resurrection of the dead."
(1 CORINTHIANS 15:21)

— Before describing all of creation as "very good," God explained that people and animals were given plants to eat (Genesis 1:29-31). In other words, animals were not being killed for food. It wasn't until after the Flood that God permitted man to eat meat (Genesis 9:3).

— Giving us a glimpse of what a "very good" world looks like, Isaiah the prophet said that one day the wolf and lamb would lie down together, and the lion would eat straw like an ox, reflecting the original state of the creation (Isaiah 11:6-9, 65:17-25).

— Romans 8:19-22 explains that the whole creation groans and is longing to be freed from the corruption brought about by man's sin. The whole creation includes animals, and the reason it suffers is because of sin.

WHEN WE LOOK AT ALL OF SCRIPTURE, IT IS EASY TO SEE THAT THE ORIGINAL WORLD CREATED BY GOD DID NOT INCLUDE DEATH AND SUFFERING OF PEOPLE OR ANIMALS. HUMAN AND ANIMAL DEATH AND SUFFERING ENTERED THIS WORLD AFTER, AND AS A RESULT OF, ADAM'S SIN.

7 C'S IN GOD'S

The Creation Museum is designed around seven pivotal events from the beginning to the end of time.

CREATION

In the beginning, God created the heavens and the earth.

Genesis 1:1

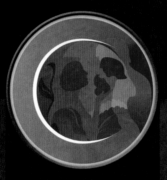

CORRUPTION

For we know that the whole creation groans and labors with birth pangs together until now.

Romans 8:22

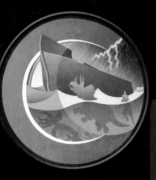

CATASTROPHE

God said, "I will bring floodwaters on the earth, to destroy from under heaven all flesh..."

Genesis 6:17

CONFUSION

The Lord confused the language of all the earth and...scattered them abroad.

Genesis 11:9

ETERNAL PLAN

As you walk through the museum, look
for signs that introduce and explain the
importance of each of these major events.

CHRIST

When the fullness of
the time had come,
God sent forth His Son,
born of a woman...

Galatians 4:4

CROSS

Christ has once
suffered for sins, the
just for the unjust...

1 Peter 3:18

CONSUMMATION

Death and Hades were
cast into the lake of fire...
And I saw a new heaven
and a new earth...

Revelation 20:14, 21:1

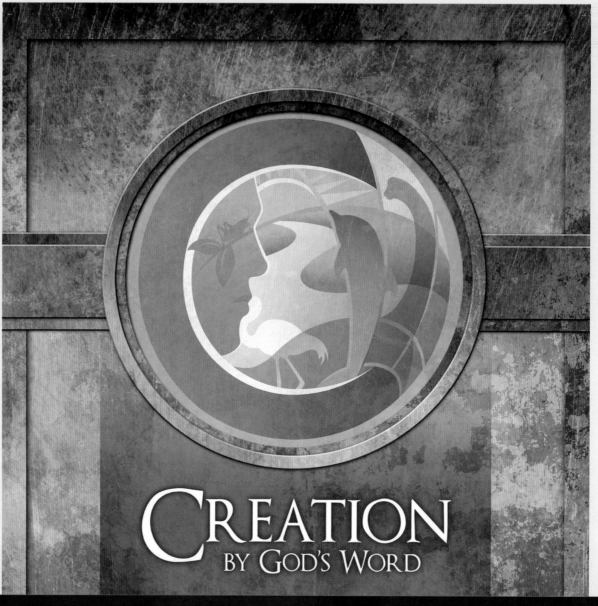

CREATION
BY GOD'S WORD

In the beginning—in six 24-hour days—
God made a perfect Creation (~4000 B.C.).

CREATION   CORRUPTION   CATASTROPHE   CONFUSION   CHRIST   CROSS   CONSUMMATION

In the beginning, God made the heavens and the earth. *Genesis 1:1*

ADAM NAMES THE ANIMALS

The Lord God brought certain animals to Adam, and he gave names to all cattle, and to the bird of the air, and to every beast of the field

—Genesis 2:19-20

HOW MANY WERE THERE?

Adam named only "birds," "cattle," and "beasts of the field"—probably only animals closely associated with man and not "beasts of the earth" or "creeping things." If the created kinds correspond to modern families, as many creation biologists believe, then Adam named fewer than two hundred animals. Naming all these animals would require only a few hours, at most.

WHAT DID THEY LOOK LIKE?

Creation biologists believe that God put the potential for a lot of variety within each created kind. With so much variety to choose from, we don't know exactly what the original representatives looked like. Some of the possibilities are displayed in this scene.

WHAT DID DINOSAURS EAT?

God said, "To every beast of the earth, and to every bird of the air, and to everything that creeps upon the earth, wherein there is life, I have given every green herb for food." —Genesis 1:30

Before man's Fall, animals were vegetarians. In a "very good" creation, no animal would die, so there were no carnivores. All the beasts of the earth, not just the "beasts of the field" that God brought to Adam to name, ate only plants.

THE TREE OF LIFE

The Lord God made to grow every tree that is pleasant to the sight and good for food; the tree of life also in the midst of the garden. —Genesis 2:9

In the garden God provided everything needed and desired for abundant life.

GOD FORMS EVE FROM ADAM'S SIDE

The Lord God said, "It is not good that man should be alone; I will make a helper fit for him" …And the rib, which the Lord God had taken from man, he made into a woman and brought her to the man.

—Genesis 2:18, 22

MALE AND FEMALE

Have you not read, that he who made them at the beginning made them male and female? —Jesus Christ

Eve (like Adam) was specially fashioned by God and did not come from an animal. Eve was not made from dust but from the side of Adam. God made male and female fit for different roles from the beginning.

ONE FLESH

For this cause a man shall leave father and mother, and shall cleave to his wife: and they two shall be one flesh. Therefore, what God has joined together, let not man separate. —Jesus Christ

DOCTRINE OF MARRIAGE

The special creation of Adam and Eve is the foundation for marriage: one man and one woman. The fact that they were one flesh is the basis for the oneness of marriage.

VERY GOOD

The Bible declares that after the Lord created Adam and Eve on the sixth day, He looked at everything He had made and it was "very good." There was no disease, suffering, bloodshed, or death in God's "very good" creation.

(Genesis 1:26–31)

GOD'S WORD

The Lord God commanded the man saying, "Of every tree of the garden you may freely eat, but of the tree of the knowledge of good and evil, you shall not eat of it, for in the day that you eat thereof you shall surely die."

—Genesis 2:16–17

WORK

The Lord God put the man into the garden of Eden to tend and keep it.

—Genesis 2:15

DOCTRINE OF WORK

In God's original design, Adam and Eve served their Creator without the burdens we have experienced since the Fall.

REST

And the evening and the morning were the sixth day. On the seventh day God ended his work, and he rested. And God blessed the seventh day.

—Genesis 1:31–2:3

Jesus said, "The Sabbath was made for man, not man for the Sabbath."

—Mark 2:27

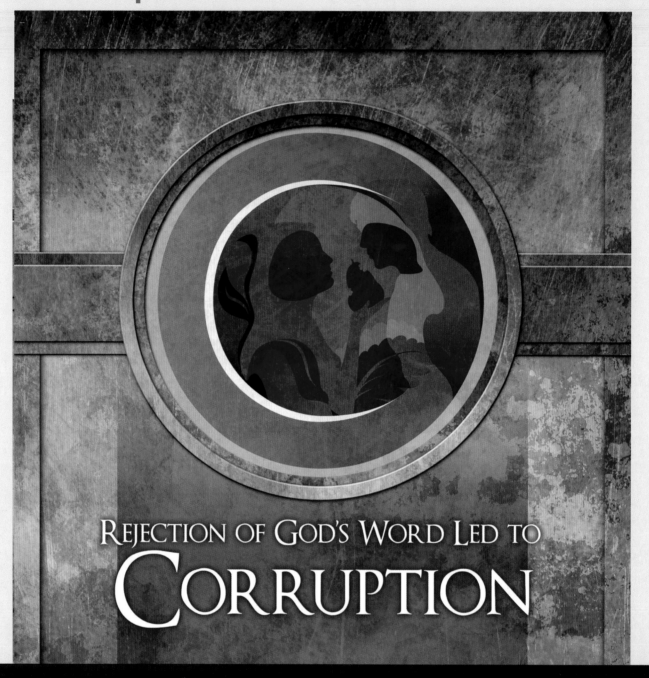

REJECTION OF GOD'S WORD LED TO
CORRUPTION

The first man, Adam, disobeyed the Creator, bringing death and corruption into creation. His disobedience explains the catastrophes, disease, suffering, and death in the present world.

CREATION   CORRUPTION   CATASTROPHE   CONFUSION   CHRIST   CROSS   CONSUMMATION

For we know that the whole creation groans and labors with birth pangs together until now. *Romans 8:22*

GOD PROMISES A SEED

The Lord God said to the serpent,
"Because you have done this, I will put
enmity between your seed and
the woman's seed; it will bruise your
head and you shall bruise his heel."

—Genesis 3:15

GOD'S WORD IS QUESTIONED AND IGNORED

The serpent said to the woman, "Has God really said
you shall not eat of every tree of the garden?" —Genesis 3:1

The woman took of the fruit and did eat, and also
gave to her husband with her, and he did eat. —Genesis 3:6

Photo by Debbie Werner AVC
Florissant Fossil Quarry

According to God's Word, thorns arose as a result of Adam's sin — just thousands, not millions, of years ago. Since thorns are a result of the curse and we have discovered them in rock layers below those containing dinosaur fossils, then these creatures must have lived after Adam sinned.

CONSEQUENCES

Adam's rebellion brought physical death into this world. The moment he disobeyed, Adam also became separated from the God who gives life to all things. This separation, called spiritual death, passed on to all of Adam's descendants.

Because of man's rebellion against his Creator, God pronounced the following judgments.

MAN

"In the sweat of your face you shall eat bread, till you return to the ground, for out of it you were taken; for dust you are and to dust you shall return." — **GENESIS 3:19**

WOMAN

"I will greatly multiply your sorrow and your conception; in sorrow you shall bring forth children; and your desire shall be to your husband, and he shall rule over you." — **GENESIS 3:16**

THE CURSE

GROUND

"**Cursed** is the ground for your sake; in sorrow you shall eat of it all the days of your life. Thorns and thistles it shall bring forth for you; and you shall eat the herb of the field." — **GENESIS 3:17–18**

SERPENT

"You are **cursed** above every beast of the field; you shall go upon your belly, and you shall eat dust all the days of your life." — **GENESIS 3:14**

COVERINGS

Although Adam and Eve deserved to die for their rebellion, God disclosed part of his permanent solution to man's sin problem. **GENESIS 3:15** *reveals that a descendant of Eve would one day defeat the serpent. Scripture later explains that this seed of the woman would also pay for our sins in full and destroy their deadly consequences.*

TEMPORARY COVERINGS

Recognizing their nakedness, Adam and Eve made coverings of fig leaves for themselves and tried to hide from God (**GENESIS 3:7–8**). But these garments were insufficient. Since "the wages of sin is death" (**ROMANS 6:23**), blood needed to be shed to cover or atone for their sin, because "the life of the flesh is in the blood" (**LEVITICUS 17:11**).

In His mercy, God made garments of skin to cover Adam and his wife (**GENESIS 3:21**). The animals God killed to provide skins to cover Adam and Eve became the first of many sacrifices to cover sin. For centuries, animals would be sacrificed for sin, but because humans are not related to animals, these sacrifices could only temporarily cover sin.

PERMANENT ATONEMENT

To permanently remove our sins, a perfect, sinless man would need to be sacrificed in our place (**HEBREWS 10:4, 11–14**).

Jesus Christ is the "last Adam" (**1 CORINTHIANS 15:45**), the seed of the woman, and the "Lamb of God" who died on the cross to take away the sin of the world (**JOHN 1:29**). Three days later, he demonstrated his power over sin and death by rising from the grave.

CAVE OF SORROWS

Sin Changed Everything

Where there was fellowship, now there is fear.

When Adam ate the fruit of the Tree of the Knowledge of Good and Evil, he disobeyed God. Because of Adam's actions, sin, death, and suffering entered the world.

Ever since that terrible moment in history, envy, hatred, and greed have driven people to commit heinous acts against other humans.

This is NOT how it was MEANT TO BE!

Everywhere around us we see the horrible effects of sin and of the curse which came as a result of sin. But God promises that a day is coming when He will judge sin and take away the curse.

[...God will wipe away every tear from their eyes; there shall be no more death, nor sorrow, nor crying. There shall be no more pain, for the former things have passed away. – Revelation 21:4

And there shall be no more curse... – Revelation 22:3]

There IS an answer to the sin problem...

[For as by one man's disobedience many were made sinners, so also by one Man's obedience many will be made righteous.

– Romans 5:19]

VENOM

BEFORE ADAM'S SIN

No venom

"And the sucking child shall play on the hole of the asp, and the weaned child shall put his hand on the viper's den" (promise of a future time, similar to Eden, Isaiah 11:8).

AFTER ADAM'S SIN

Though nothing harmed animals before Adam's sin, venom harms animals in the present. We do not know exactly how venoms first entered the world. Possibilities include:

> *Changed use of chemicals* (chemicals that once had non-harmful functions at the creation changed to venoms after the Curse).

> *Revealed information* (the potential to make venoms was built into the original creation, but not revealed until after the Curse).

DEATH

BEFORE ADAM'S SIN

No death

According to the Bible, animals and humans have "life" (Hebrew *nephesh*), but plants do not. So humans and animals were created to eat plants, and in the original world before sin, humans and animals would never die.

AFTER ADAM'S SIN

Death was introduced after Adam's sin.

> Death of humans is a judgment on man's rebellion.

> Death is our "enemy," according to the Apostle Paul, which invaded God's "very good" creation (1 Corinthians 15:26).

DISEASE

BEFORE ADAM'S SIN

No disease

"There shall be no more pain" (promise of a future time, similar to Eden, Revelation 21:4).

AFTER ADAM'S SIN

Disease entered the creation after Adam's sin:

> genetic mistakes (mutations)

> excessive cell reproduction rates (cancer)

> taking more than giving (parasitism)

CARNIVORES

BEFORE ADAM'S SIN

No carnivores

God said, "To every beast of the earth I have given every green herb for food" (Genesis 1:30).

AFTER ADAM'S SIN

Though all animals ate plants before Adam's sin, some are carnivores in this present fallen world. We do not know how meat eating first entered the world. Possibilities include:

› *Changed diet* (the diet of some animals merely changed)

› *Revealed information* (the potential for meat eating was placed into the original creation, but not revealed until after the Curse).

By removing the weakest and diseased, carnivores help keep the fallen world functioning despite sin.

RED TOOTH AND CLAW

BEFORE ADAM'S SIN

No struggle for survival

"They shall not hurt nor destroy in all my holy mountain" (promise of a future time, similar to Eden, Isaiah 11:9)

AFTER ADAM'S SIN

After Adam's sin, animals must overproduce to replace the dead and diseased. As a result:

› Animals struggle for limited resources ("nature red in tooth and claw").

› The weakest animals die off (natural selection).

These processes help keep the fallen world functioning despite sin.

SCAVENGERS

BEFORE ADAM'S SIN

No scavengers of animals

Before Adam's sin, scavengers were designed to clean the world of excess plant material and return chemicals to the nutrient cycles.

AFTER ADAM'S SIN

Once death entered the world, scavengers were necessary to scavenge bodies of animals to keep the world clean and return chemicals to the nutrient cycles. We do not know exactly how scavenging of flesh was introduced into the world. Possibilities include:

› *Changed diet* (diets merely changed, as animals that scavenged plants at the creation began scavenging animal flesh).

› *Revealed information* (the potential to scavenge meat was placed into the original creation, but not revealed until after the Curse).

› *Fallen creation* (God gave some organisms the ability to scavenge flesh at the time of the Curse).

COSMIC AGING

BEFORE ADAM'S SIN

No aging in the universe

In the original creation before Adam's sin, humans would never die. This suggests that the creation was originally made to last forever.

AFTER ADAM'S SIN

The universe began aging.

"The earth and the heavens....shall perish. Yes, all of them... shall wax old" (Psalm 102:25-26).

COSMIC PAIN

The whole creation groans and travails in pain together until now (Romans 8:22).

With Adam's sin, death and suffering entered the creation for the first time. Disease and natural catastrophes also began at this time. The creation is no longer perfect, as God originally designed it, because in Adam we committed high treason against the God of creation.

CONFLICT

BEFORE ADAM'S SIN

No conflict

"The wolf shall dwell with the lamb, and the leopard shall lie down with the kid; and the calf and the young lion and the fatling together; and a little child shall lead them" (promise of a future time, similar to Eden, Isaiah 11:6).

AFTER ADAM'S SIN

With the entrance of sin, conflict entered the world:

- → animals against animals
- → animals against humans
- → humans against humans

105

Exhibit: **Corruption**

POISONS

BEFORE ADAM'S SIN

No poisons

"They shall not hurt nor destroy in all my holy mountain," says the Lord (promise of a future time, similar to Eden, Isaiah 65:25).

AFTER ADAM'S SIN

Once animals began overproducing to replace the dead and diseased, they would eat too many plants. So God protected some plants with poisons and other defenses. We do not know exactly how poisons first entered the world. Possibilities include:

> *Changed use of chemicals* (chemicals that once had non-harmful functions at the creation were changed to poisons after the Curse).

> *Hidden information* (the potential to make poisons was built into the original creation, but not revealed until after the Curse).

WEEDS

BEFORE ADAM'S SIN

No weeds

God created a perfect balance in the beginning, as plants produced exactly the amount of food needed by the animals of the earth.

AFTER ADAM'S SIN

Once animals began overproducing to replace the dead and diseased, they would eat too many plants. So God introduced overproduction of plants to replace the plants that would be lost.

As a result:

> Plants struggle against other plants for survival.

> Plants grow where they are not wanted (weeds).

BURDENSOME WORK

BEFORE ADAM'S SIN

No burdensome work

"They shall not labor in vain" (promise of a future time, similar to Eden, Isaiah 65:23).

AFTER ADAM'S SIN

God cursed the ground because of Adam's sin, so that he had to make bread "by the sweat of his face" (Genesis 3:19). Weeds and disease required more work to harvest crops—to pull weeds, to fight disease, to provide nutrients.

SUFFERING

BEFORE ADAM'S SIN

No suffering

"God shall wipe away all tears from their eyes, and there shall be neither sorrow nor crying" (promise of a future time, similar to Eden, Revelation 21:4)

AFTER ADAM'S SIN

When disease, death, conflict, and sin entered the world, then

> the pain of childbirth increased

> physical suffering began

> emotional suffering began

CAIN MURDERS ABEL

Eve conceived and bore Cain. She again bore his brother Abel. In the process of time. Cain brought of the fruit of the ground and offering to the Lord. Abel also brought of the firstlings of his flock and of their fat. And the Lord had respect to Abel and to his offering, but not to Cain and to his offering. And Cain was very angry. . . . And Cain rose up against Abel his brother a slew him. —Genesis 4:1–5, 8

WHERE DID CAIN GET HIS WIFE?

Cain went out from the presence of the Lord and dwelt in the land of Nod, on the east of Eden. And Cain knew his wife, and she conceived and bore Enoch (Genesis 4:16-17).

The Bible teaches that Adam was "the first man" and that Eve was the "mother of all living" (1 Corinthians 15:45; Genesis 3:20). All humans are descendants of these two people.

Genesis 5:4 teaches that Adam and Eve had sons and daughters. So, originally, brothers had to marry sisters.

Before jumping to conclusions, realize that

1. All humans are related. So whenever someone gets married, they marry their relative.

2. One of the most honored men of the Bible, Abraham, was married to his half sister. It wasn't until much later that God instructed the Israelites not to marry close relatives— a principle we follow today.

3. When close relatives marry today, there is an increased likelihood of deformities in the offspring because of the mutations (mistakes) that have accumulated in the human race since Adam's sin. The closer the relatives, the more likelihood such people will have similar mistakes. If these mutations are inherited in offspring from both parents, then there is an increased probability of major physiological problems.

4. The farther back in history one goes (back towards the Fall of Adam), the less of a problem mutations in the human population would be. At the time of Adam and Eve's children, there would have been very few mutations in the human genome—thus close relatives could marry, and provided it was one man for one woman (the biblical doctrine of marriage), there was nothing wrong with close relatives marrying in early biblical history.

5. In present usage, the word *incest* includes both the marriage of close relatives and any sexual activity between close relatives who are not married. Sexual activity outside of the bounds of marriage, whether between near relatives or not, has been wrong from the beginning. Marriage between close relatives, however, was not a problem in early biblical history.

6. Since God is the One who defined marriage in the first place, God's Word is the only standard for defining proper marriage. People who do not accept the Bible as their absolute authority have no basis for condemning someone like Cain marrying his sister.

ABEL'S WALK OF FAITH

PLEASED GOD
"By faith Abel offered to God a more excellent sacrifice than Cain" (Hebrews 11:4a).

RIGHTEOUS
"Abel obtained witness that he was righteous" (Hebrews 11:4b).

DWELLS WITH GOD
"Therefore, God has prepared for [Abel] a city" (Hebrews 11:16).

WAY OF CAIN

REJECTED GOD
"Cain slew his brother because his own works were evil and his brother's righteous" (I John 3:12).

Cain had a rebellious heart against God when he offered a sacrifice of the fruit of the ground.

UNRIGHTEOUS
"And the Lord said to Cain, 'Why are you angry? If you do well, shall you not be accepted?'" (Genesis 4:6-7).

But in response to Cain's sin, God offered a solution— to repent and "do well." Cain further sinned by rejecting the solution.

JUDGMENT
"The Lord said to Cain, 'You are cursed.' And Cain said to the Lord, 'My punishment is greater than I can bear.' And Cain went out from the presence of the Lord" (Genesis 4:11, 13, 16).

The way of Cain, rebellion against God, leads to separation from God, both now and forever.

Methuselah

The oldest man on record is Methuselah, died just before Noah's Flood, at the ripe old age of 969 years. During Methuselah's lifetime, he saw how mankind had forgotten all about God. People had chosen to live their own way and the "wickedness of man was great in the earth, and every intent of the thoughts of his heart was only evil continually" (Genesis 6:5). God told Methuselah's grandson, Noah, that He was going to send a global Flood to destroy the earth. God instructed Noah to build a huge ship—an Ark—to save representatives of every land-dwelling, air-breathing animal, his family, and Noah from the coming global judgment.

GOD KEEPS HIS PROMISES

fter Cain killed Abel, God gave Eve another son who would continue the line of the Promised Seed. "Eve bore a son and called his name Seth ['Appointed' in Hebrew]. 'For God,' she said, 'has appointed me another seed instead of Abel, whom Cain slew' " (Genesis 4:25).

Through Seth, God kept alive the line of the Promised Seed. The longest-living person in that line was Methuselah (depicted in this scene). He lived long enough to see his grandson, Noah, build the Ark before he died at age 969.

SEED OF THE WOMAN

SEED OF THE WOMAN	YOU SHALL SURELY DIE	
Adam begat Seth	Adam lived 930 years	and he died.
Seth begat Enosh	Seth lived 912 years	and he died.
Enosh begat Kenan	Enosh lived 905 years	and he died.
Kenan begat Mahalalel	Kenan lived 910 years	and he died.
Mahalalel begat Jared	Mahalalel lived 895 years	and he died.
Jared begat Enoch	Jared lived 962 years	and he died.
Enoch begat Methuselah	Enoch walked with God 300 years	and God took him.
Methuselah begat Lamech	Methuselah lived 969 years	and he died.
Lamech begat Noah	Lamech lived 777 years	and he died.
And Noah begat Shem, Ham, and Japheth.		

—Genesis 5:3-32

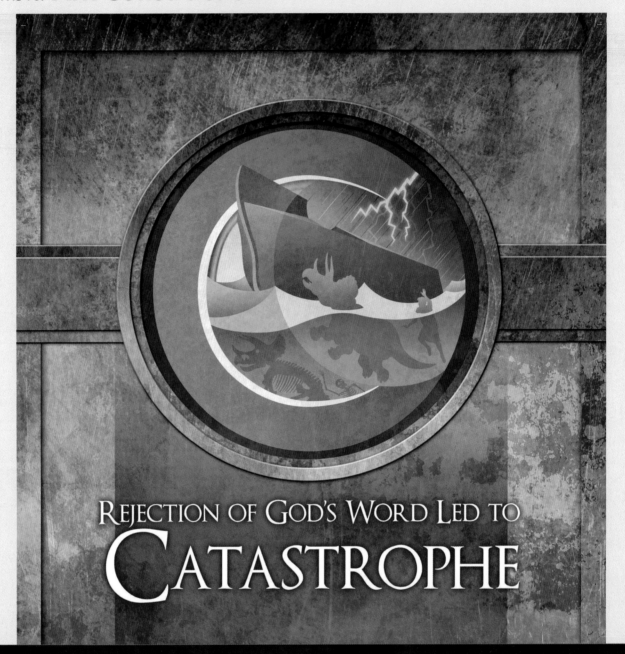

REJECTION OF GOD'S WORD LED TO
CATASTROPHE

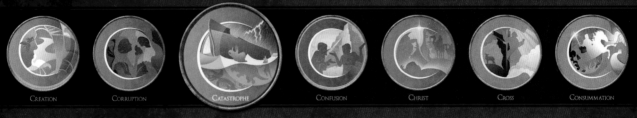

Adam's race became so wicked that God judged the earth with the catastrophic, global Flood, saving only those on the Ark built by Noah (~2350 B.C.). This global catastrophe resulted in fossils all over the earth.

CREATION CORRUPTION CATASTROPHE CONFUSION CHRIST CROSS CONSUMMATION

God said, "I will bring a flood of waters upon the earth, to destroy all flesh." *Genesis 6:17*

NOAH PREACHES RIGHTEOUSNESS

God spared not the old world, but saved Noah, a preacher of righteousness.

—2 Peter 2:5

BRONZE AND IRON

Zillah also gave birth to Tubal-Cain, who made all kinds of bronze and iron tools (Genesis 4:22).

Before the Flood, Tubal-Cain taught others how to work with metals, including iron. So Noah could have had access to bronze or iron tools. He may have also used metal fasteners in the construction of the Ark.

THE CUBIT

A cubit is a common measurement used by a number of ancient cultures in the Middle East. The cubit is equal to the distance between a person's elbow and fingertip.

Modern units of distance, such as the meter or foot, are standardized. However, in ancient times, cubit lengths were not consistent across cultures. Consequently, a variety of cubit lengths were used. The normal cubit length in biblical times is estimated between 17.5 inches to 18 inches.

Many ancient construction projects were built using a royal cubit, which adds the width of four fingers (approximately three inches) to the standard cubit.

Our sister attraction, the Ark Encounter, utilized a cubit length of 20.4 inches, which is close to one of the shortest royal cubits on record. Based on this cubit, the Ark Encounter measures 510 feet long, 85 feet wide, and 51 feet high, and its volume is about 1.88 million cubic feet, large enough to contain approximately 450 semi-truck trailers.

HOW BIG WAS THE ARK?

The length of the Ark shall be three hundred cubits (Genesis 6:15).

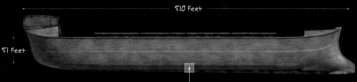

510 Feet

51 Feet

Note: The exhibit in this room represents less than 1% of the volume of the biblical Ark.

The scale of the Ark is dramatic, and as demonstrated by the ancient Greeks and fifteenth-century Chinese shipbuilders, the Ark is tantalizingly close to the limits of known wooden shipbuilding technology. With no need for tall masts and without the economic restrictions of nineteenth-century shipwrights, the hull of the Ark could be made incredibly strong using ordinary wood and simple tools.

GOPHER WOOD

Make an Ark of gopher wood; you shall make rooms in the Ark and cover it with pitch inside and out (Genesis 6:14).

While Noah made the Ark out of gopher wood, we cannot be certain what modern tree, if any, corresponds to the timbers used to build Noah's Ark. The term gopher wood is only found in Genesis 6:14.

Some Bible versions translate the term for gopher wood as cypress, and cedar has also been mentioned as a possible choice for the Ark's wood. However, these guesses are largely based on the mistaken notion that Noah built the Ark in the Middle East. Prior to the Flood, the earth was very different, and there is no way for us to know where Noah built the Ark. Ultimately, we cannot positively identify gopher wood today.

PITCH

And cover it inside and outside with pitch (Genesis 6:14).

The source of the pitch for Noah's Ark is not known. It could have been bitumen or gums extracted from plant resins. The process of manufacturing pitch from pine resin has ancient origins. Wooden ships were waterproofed by pitch from tree resins well before the oil industry was born. The core ingredient of plant resin pitch is gum rosin.

Depending on the source and how it is cooked, plant-derived pitch can vary in color from light amber to almost black.

TRUNNELS (TREE NAILS)

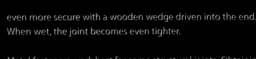

When used correctly, wooden nails (tree nails or trunnels) can be superior to metal for attaching planks. To form these wooden nails, ship makers must choose a harder wood than the plank and shape it into dowels. Once hammered into the pre-drilled hole, the wood soon absorbs moisture and swells. This helps it grip tightly and make a permanent watertight seal. The end is sawn off and the joint can be made even more secure with a wooden wedge driven into the end. When wet, the joint becomes even tighter.

Metal fasteners work best for some structural joints. Obtaining these fasteners would not have been a problem for Noah because men knew how to work with bronze and iron (Genesis 4:22).

PLANKING

The ancient Greeks built ships with edge-jointed planking, which is an ideal solution to plank shear, a problem that plagued European shipwrights only a few centuries ago. Whether this practice was forgotten or simply too laborious for modern shipbuilders, it allowed the Greeks to build the almost Ark-scale *Tessarakonteres* (420 feet, 128 m).

Multiple layers of planking also increase hull strength. If Noah used these methods, the Ark would probably not have had problems with water seepage during its single voyage that lasted a maximum of five months.

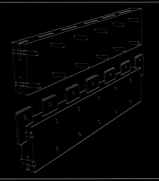

THE TESTIMONY OF THE ARK

The Ark itself would have been like a billboard, a bold statement of Noah's faith, warning of the coming Flood. The huge ship built for the saving of Noah's household (Hebrews 11:7) would have been a constant reminder of the impending judgment to all who saw it.

UNCHANGING PROMISES

GOD'S IMAGE
"In the image of God he made man" (Genesis 9:6).

MAN'S DOMINION
"Be fruitful and multiply and fill the earth. Every beast of the field, and every bird of the air, and every fish of the sea, into your hand they are delivered" (Genesis 9:1-2).

EARTH'S PROVISION
"While the earth remains, seedtime and harvest, and cold and heat, and summer and winter, and day and night shall not cease" (Genesis 8:22).

There have been many floods since the time of Noah, but never another worldwide Flood. Through that great Flood, God destroyed the old world and preserved His seed. After the Flood, Noah pleased God with a sacrifice, and God responded by renewing His promises.

CHANGED RELATIONSHIPS

BLOOD REQUIRED
"Whoever sheds man's blood, his blood shall be shed by man" (Genesis 9:6).

MAN FEARED
"And the fear of you and the dread of you shall be upon all that moves on the earth and upon all the fish of the sea" (Genesis 9:3).

MEAT ALLOWED
"Every moving thing that lives shall be food for you" (Genesis 9:3).

God's words to Noah suggest that several things familiar to us in the present were different before the Flood. For example, murder was apparently not punishable by death, and animals were not afraid of man. Also, while fossils of animals buried in the Flood show that some animals were already eating other animals, God waited until after the Flood to allow man to eat animals.

GOD RENEWS HIS PROMISES

I established my covenant with you and with your seed after you, and with every living creature that is with you; neither shall there any more be a flood to destroy the earth. . . . This is the token of the covenant, the bow shall be in the cloud and I will look upon it that I may remember the covenant.
—Genesis 9:9–12, 14, 16

THE FLOOD BURIES LIFE

ORGANISMS WERE BURIED IN SEQUENCE DURING THE FLOOD

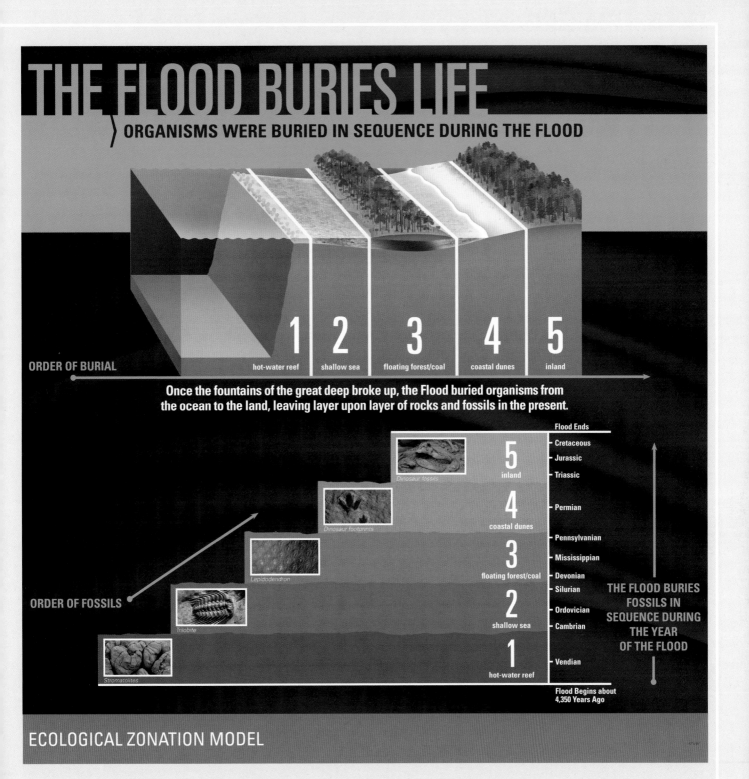

ORDER OF BURIAL

1	2	3	4	5
hot-water reef	shallow sea	floating forest/coal	coastal dunes	inland

Once the fountains of the great deep broke up, the Flood buried organisms from the ocean to the land, leaving layer upon layer of rocks and fossils in the present.

ORDER OF FOSSILS

Dinosaur fossils

Dinosaur footprints

Lepidodendron

Trilobite

Stromatolites

5 — inland
4 — coastal dunes
3 — floating forest/coal
2 — shallow sea
1 — hot-water reef

Flood Ends
- Cretaceous
- Jurassic
- Triassic
- Permian
- Pennsylvanian
- Mississippian
- Devonian
- Silurian
- Ordovician
- Cambrian
- Vendian

Flood Begins about 4,350 Years Ago

THE FLOOD BURIES FOSSILS IN SEQUENCE DURING THE YEAR OF THE FLOOD

ECOLOGICAL ZONATION MODEL

DEEP OCEAN

CATASTROPHIC PLATE TECTONICS (CPT) MODEL

In this model, the Flood began with the breakup of the earth's crust by the springs of the great deep. Then huge rifts opened on the ocean floor, and molten rock contacted ocean water, creating huge, linear geysers across the earth's surface.

The water waves generated by this deep ocean upheaval rapidly moved landwards and progressively destroyed and buried various proposed pre-Flood ecosystems (biomes) in a distinctive order that we now see in the fossil record.

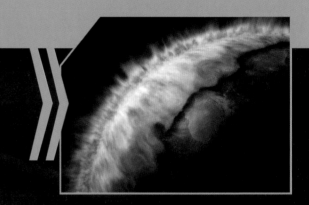

1) HOT-WATER REEFS

HYDROTHERMAL BIOME MODEL

4,350 YEARS AGO

In the CPT model, the breakup of the earth's crust created a series of enormous earthquakes. These earthquakes collapsed the edge of the continental plates. Whatever was on those continental edges, such as the hot-water stromatolite reefs ecosystem, avalanched into deeper water.

In the lowermost fossil layers, we find stromatolites, which may be evidence of pre-Flood hot-water reefs inhabited almost exclusively by bacteria.

TODAY

2) SHALLOW SEAFLOOR

SHALLOW SEAFLOOR BIOMES MODEL

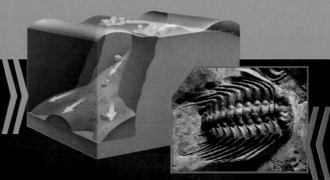

4,350 YEARS AGO

Building further on the CPT model, the earthquakes caused by the breakup of the earth's crust generated enormous Flood waves which passed over the stromatolite reefs and began destroying the shallow seafloor ecosystems on the possible wide underwater continental shelves. This stage of the ecological zonation model has ecosystem after ecosystem being carried farther out to sea and buried.

Above Vendian stromatolites, we find fossils from many exotic ocean environments, including thousands of trilobite species.

TODAY

3) COAL

AUSTIN FLOATING LOG MAT MODEL

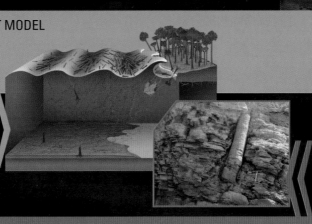

4,350 YEARS AGO

This model is based on the destruction of the trees in the middle of possible floating forests creating log mats of billions of tree trunks. Bark rubbed off the floating logs became waterlogged and sank to the ocean bottom. As the bark layers were buried, they were compressed and coalified into coal seams. Observations at Spirit Lake after the devastation of Mt. St. Helens in the 1980s confirm this model.

In the layers at the top of the sequence of plant fossils, upright tree trunks are found sitting on top of flat-topped coal seams.

TODAY

3) FLOATING FOREST

FLOATING FOREST BIOME MODEL

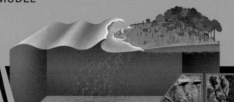

4,350 YEARS AGO

Assuming the CPT model, as waves grew large enough, they began ripping apart what were possibly floating forests, from the outside edge inward. In a sequence reflecting the forest structure, plants torn off the forest became waterlogged, sank, and were buried on the ocean bottom.

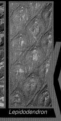

Cooksonia   *Archaeopteris*   *Lepidodendron*

We find exotic plant fossils in a regular sequence from small plants to trees, possible evidence of a huge pre-Flood floating forest.

TODAY

4) COASTAL DUNES

COASTAL PERMO-TRIASSIC SANDS MODEL

4,350 YEARS AGO

Tidal waves hit the shorelines and tore apart beaches and dunes. Sand and animals were dragged out to sea and deposited in thick layers.

Above the Carboniferous coals, extensive sandstone deposits are found on all the world's continents.

TODAY

5) INLAND

EXOTIC LAND BIOMES MODEL

4,350 YEARS AGO

As the sea level rose, Flood waves reached farther and farther inland. This model has ecosystem after ecosystem of subsequent plants and animals being carried out to sea and buried.

Above the Permo-Triassic sandstones, we find fossils from exotic land communities, including hundreds of dinosaur species.

TODAY

THE KEY: GOD'S WORD

THE PRESENT IS NOT THE KEY TO THE PAST

Noah's Flood and times following involved more violent catastrophism than anything known in the present.

At best, modern catastrophes provide only clues about those times.

RESIDUAL CATASTROPHISM MODEL

THE FLOOD DROWNS THE EARTH

> THE FLOOD COVERED ALL THE CONTINENTS

THE FLOOD WAS A GLOBAL JUDGMENT

Human violence was worldwide, so judgment had to be worldwide. Animal violence was everywhere, so animals everywhere had to be destroyed. All land was cursed, so all land had to be restored.

THE FLOOD WAS A GLOBAL CATASTROPHE

The Bible states the Flood covered all mountains, so the Flood had to cover all land on earth. The Bible states the Flood lasted over a year, so the Flood was not merely a local event.

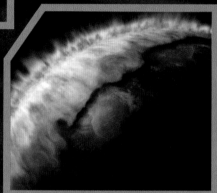

THE FLOOD REARRANGES THE EARTH

> CONTINENTS MOVED RAPIDLY DURING THE FLOOD

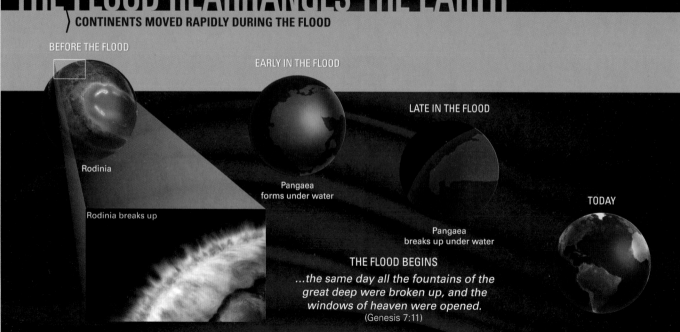

BEFORE THE FLOOD

EARLY IN THE FLOOD

LATE IN THE FLOOD

Rodinia

Rodinia breaks up

Pangaea forms under water

Pangaea breaks up under water

TODAY

THE FLOOD BEGINS

...the same day all the fountains of the great deep were broken up, and the windows of heaven were opened.
(Genesis 7:11)

⟩A CLUE: MOUNT ST. HELENS

THE PRESENT PROVIDES HINTS ABOUT THE PAST

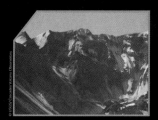

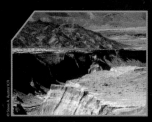

A SMALL CATASTROPHE IN THE PRESENT HELPS US UNDERSTAND A HUGE CATASTROPHE IN THE PAST.

① ASH CLOUD

A single ash cloud cools the earth a fraction of a degree.

A miniature example of the earth cooling after the Flood

② LAVA DOME

When 11 years old, a new lava dome dates greater than 350,000 years old by potassium-argon (K-Ar) dating.

An example of radioisotope dating difficulties

③ LOOWIT CANYON AND STEP CANYON

Mudflows cut canyons out of solid rock in just a few years.

A miniature example of rapid erosion during and immediately after the Flood

④ ENGINEERS CANYON AND LITTLE GRAND CANYON

Mudflows cut canyons out of soft sediment in hours.

A miniature example of rapid erosion during and immediately after the Flood

Exhibit: **Flood Geology**

⑤ PYROCLASTIC DEPOSITS

Pyroclastic flows (fluid hot ash) deposit 25 feet of finely layered sediments in a few hours.

A miniature example of rapid sedimentation during and immediately after the Flood

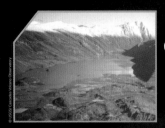

⑥ COLDWATER DELTA

Hundreds of feet of delta form in just a few years.

A miniature picture of delta formation during and after the Flood

⑦ ELK RECOVERY

Thousands of elk killed in the eruption are replaced within a decade.

A clue about how animals refilled the earth after the Flood

⑧ PLANT RECOVERY

Ecosystems develop in years rather than decades.

A small picture of the rapid development of ecosystems after the Flood

⑨ VERTICAL FLOATING LOGS

Uprooted trees float vertically and sink to the bottom of Spirit Lake.

A clue about how petrified forests and polystrate fossils formed as a result of the Flood

⑩ BARK PEAT

Bark rubs off floating logs and accumulates at the bottom of Spirit Lake.

A clue about how coal layers formed as a result of the Flood

THE FLOOD...
RECORDED IN THE ROCKS

THE FLOOD WAS ENORMOUS
A SCALE NEVER SEEN BEFORE OR SINCE

In our own **backyards** we can see the layers rain produces on a small scale.

Occasional catastrophes, like the explosion of **Mount St. Helens**, produce similar layers, but on a larger scale.

Around the world, we find similar layers on an **even larger** scale. To explain those layers, it is reasonable to infer similar, but larger, catastrophes.

There are even layers of such **enormous** scale as to be consistent with a global catastrophe.

BACKYARD SCALE
LOCAL FLOODS (OBSERVED)

River floods commonly erode and deposit less than 1/1000 cubic miles of sand and mud in minutes to hours.

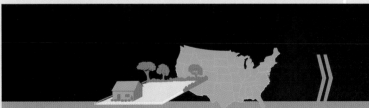

BACKYARD

COUNTY SCALE
COUNTY-SIZED FLOODS (OBSERVED)

The Mount St. Helens catastrophe eroded and deposited 0.7 cubic miles of sand and mud in minutes.

STATE SCALE
STATE-SIZED FLOODS (INFERRED)

The drainage of glacial Lake Missoula, formed soon after the Flood, required only a few days to erode and deposit almost 50 cubic miles of gravel, sand, and mud.

BRETZ COLUMBIA RIVER FLOOD MODEL

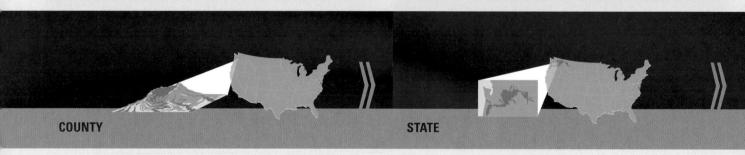

COUNTY

STATE

REGIONAL SCALE
› REGION-SIZED FLOODS (INFERRED)

The drainage of a huge lake system, formed soon after the Flood, required only a few weeks to erode and deposit about 1000 cubic miles of gravel, sand, and mud.

GLOBAL SCALE
› GLOBAL FLOOD (INFERRED)

The Flood required only a few months to deposit about 10,000,000 cubic miles of gravel, sand, and mud.

BREACHED DAM MODEL

GLOBAL FLOOD MODEL

REGIONAL

GLOBAL

125

THE FLOOD BURIES THE EARTH

> THE FLOOD COVERED ALL THE CONTINENTS IN SEDIMENT

Evidences of the Flood in Grand Canyon

SEA ANIMALS FAR ABOVE SEA LEVEL

① SPONGE FOSSILS

The Kaibab Limestone is nearly a mile above sea level, yet it contains beautiful marine sponge fossils.

③ NAUTILOID FOSSILS

Thousands of feet above sea level, the Redwall Limestone has abundant fossils, including billions of nautiloids.

④ FOSSILS OF TRILOBITES, WORMS, ETC.

Abundant, well-preserved fossils suggest rapid, thick deposition.

SAND CARRIED ACROSS CONTINENTS

② SAND FROM THE APPALACHIANS

Sand grains in the Coconino Sandstone come from the Appalachian Mountains.

DEEP AND WIDE EROSION

① WIDE, FLAT SURFACE

Lack of rocks above the Kaibab Limestone and nothing downstream suggest sheet erosion over a huge area.

⑤ THE GREAT UNCONFORMITY

The near-flat erosion surface under the Tapeats Sandstone suggests massive sheet erosion.

LAYERS OVER CONTINENTS

② COCONINO SANDSTONE

The Coconino Sandstone covers 300,000 square miles of area in western North America.

③ REDWALL LIMESTONE

The Redwall Limestone is continuous with limestones across the United States, including the rocks where Mammoth Cave is found in Kentucky.

⑤ TAPEATS SANDSTONE

The Tapeats Sandstone is continuous with sheet sandstones covering most of North America.

RAPID, THICK DEPOSITION

② SAND HUNDREDS OF FEET THICK

The Coconino Sandstone is several hundred feet thick. Huge crossbeds suggest rapid, thick deposition.

③ BILLIONS OF NAUTILOIDS

A six-foot layer containing billions of nautiloids suggests rapid deposition.

④ MULTIPLE, THIN LAYERS

Abundant, well-preserved fossils suggest rapid, thick deposition.
Thin layers also suggest rapid deposition.

① THROUGH ⑤ DEFORMATION OF MULTIPLE LAYERS

Tight bending of the Tapeats Sandstone through the Kaibab Formation suggests one mile of sediment was deposited quickly and was still soft when bent.

⟩CANYONS ERODE

CANYONS WERE CARVED RAPIDLY AFTER THE FLOOD

Rapid erosion is indicated by the small difference in age between lake deposits upstream and surge deposits downstream.

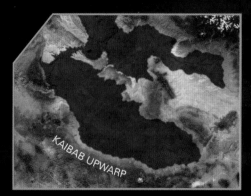

After Noah's Flood ended, lakes filled up behind the Kaibab Upwarp.

The water in each lake broke through, carved Grand Canyon, stripped slopes clean, and drained away.

1000 cubic miles of sediment, which eroded from Grand Canyon and the lake region above, are now downstream in the Salton Sea trough.

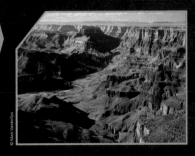

① COLORADO RIVER

The current Colorado River does not cut downward, suggesting that modern erosion cannot explain Grand Canyon.

② UINKARET VOLCANOES

Basalt lavas dated by different methods give very different dates, suggesting radioactive decay rates were faster in the past.

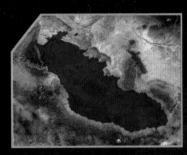

③ HOPI LAKE

The evidence indicates that a lake formed after the Flood and then drained away. Clean slopes without eroded debris (talus) indicate that erosion was recent, without enough time to form talus.

④ SURGE DEPOSITS

The kind and quantity of sediments eroded from Grand Canyon are now found downstream. These "surge deposits" formed in surging floods, suggesting very rapid erosion of Grand Canyon.

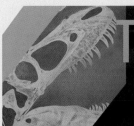

THE FLOOD...
RECORDED IN THE FOSSILS

>THE FLOOD RECEDES
CONTINENTS WERE SCOURED BY RETREATING FLOOD WATERS

Flood waters dropped thousands of feet of mud and sand onto the world's continents. Retreating Flood waters swept some of that pile of sediment away.

① KAIBAB UPWARP

Warping in late Flood times left a fold in the crust known as the Kaibab Upwarp. At that time there was probably another mile of sediment over this area.

② GRAND STAIRCASE

Retreating Flood waters scoured nearly a mile of sediment off the top of the Kaibab Upwarp. Cliffs of harder material make up the "steps" in the Grand Staircase.

③ RED BUTTE AND CEDAR MOUNTAIN

"Islands" of sediment, such as Red Butte and Cedar Mountain, were left behind by receding Flood waters.

WHAT HAPPENED TO THE DINOSAURS?

FOSSILS GIVE CLUES

There are still many mysteries surrounding dinosaurs. We know they are specific types of land animals that were created on Day 6 along with man, but they have since gone extinct. So we are left to wonder how they lived, what they looked like, and what they ate; and we especially wonder what happened to them. How did a group of animals that left fossilized footprints on every continent eventually cease to exist? The fossils contain clues about these mysteries, but we still don't know the whole story.

Paleontologists who believe in evolution have all sorts of ideas for why dinosaurs are no longer here. Some suggest that an asteroid struck the earth or that many huge volcanoes erupted simultaneously, causing dinosaurs to go extinct. As a consequence, some say the dinosaurs that survived those blasts starved to death, while others say they died of overeating. However, these scientists don't have the full story because they don't start with the eyewitness account of creation that God gave to us in His Word, the Bible.

Paleontologists who believe that God created the earth in six days as recorded in the Bible have a different answer to the question about dinosaurs. These scientists conclude that most of the dinosaurs died in the global Flood.

So why did the dinosaurs that survived the Flood on Noah's Ark eventually go extinct? The dinosaur kinds that Noah took with him exited the Ark into a vastly different environment. They, along with other now-extinct animal kinds, died out due to competition for food, a post-Flood Ice Age, or other post-Flood catastrophes, or maybe even because people killed them for food or sport.

Genesis 1:24–25

SCIENTISTS WHO STUDY DINOSAUR FOSSILS TO LEARN ABOUT THE PAST ARE CALLED PALEONTOLOGISTS.

WE HAVE TO FILL IN THE MISSING DETAILS BASED ON OUR WORLDVIEW—OUR STARTING POINTS. WE ALL HAVE THE SAME FOSSILS, THE SAME FACTS, AND THE SAME EVIDENCE. OUR BELIEFS ABOUT HOW THE EARTH WAS FORMED SHAPE OUR INTERPRETATION OF THE EVIDENCE.

MANY OF THE DINOSAURS WERE WASHED TOGETHER BY THE SWIRLING FLOOD WATERS AND BURIED IN THE RAPIDLY FORMING SEDIMENTARY LAYERS, RESULTING IN MASSIVE BONE BEDS OF DISARTICULATED DINOSAUR FOSSILS LIKE MOST OF THOSE FOUND AT DINOSAUR NATIONAL MONUMENT.

OTHER DINOSAURS, LIKE EBENEZER, WERE BURIED IN SEDIMENT, REMAINING ESSENTIALLY ARTICULATED AND INTACT.

WHO AM I? ···· ········ ···

MEET EBENEZER THE ALLOSAURUS

The name *Allosaurus* means "other lizard." *Allosaurus* belongs to the suborder of dinosaurs that contains theropods, meaning "beast feet." While not as well-known as the larger theropod *Tyrannosaurus*, the *Allosaurus* also seems to have been a formidable, carnivorous dinosaur. Theropod and *Allosaurus* are the scientific names for this dinosaur that give us information about him, but he also has been given a personal pet name to distinguish him from other *Allosaurus* skeletons that have been found elsewhere. His personal name is Ebenezer.

NAME ORIGINS

Our Ebenezer isn't named after the miserly character found in Charles Dickens's well-known tale, *A Christmas Carol*. Instead, his name comes from the Bible. In 1 Samuel 7, it is recorded that God rescued the Israelites from the terror of the Philistine army. Afterward, the prophet Samuel set up a rock to remember God's help and called it "Ebenezer," which means "the stone of help." Some of the people involved in excavating this dinosaur named him Ebenezer because they saw him as a reminder of God's judgment of the world and how He preserved mankind and animal kinds on Noah's Ark.

> A **CARNIVORE** IS SOMETHING THAT EATS MOSTLY MEAT. HOWEVER, BEFORE SIN ENTERED THE WORLD, THERE WERE NO CARNIVORES. ALL ANIMALS AND HUMANS ATE ONLY PLANTS.[1]
> [1]See Genesis 1–3.

WHAT WAS FOUND?

DETAILS FROM THE DIG

This animal was found buried lying on its left side, its skeleton essentially intact with the bones still mostly articulated and laid out in the correct anatomical order. The skeleton was oriented with the head at the western end and the tail pointed southeast. The remains of the animal's spine, which consists of the vertebrae running from the base of the skull to the tip of the tail, were found lying in a curved alignment. While the neck vertebrae were still attached to the skull, they and the skull were broken off from the spine. But many of the tail vertebrae were present and still articulated. The hyoid bones (tongue bones) were also found intact in the correct anatomical position within the skull—an exceedingly rare circumstance.

> **ARTICULATED** MEANS THAT THE BONES WERE STILL IN THE SAME RELATIVE POSITION TO EACH OTHER AS THEY WERE WHEN THE ANIMAL WAS ALIVE.

Due to erosion of the hillside he was found in, most of Ebenezer's limb bones and mid-section were not recovered.

SOME ASSEMBLY REQUIRED

This skeleton is assembled from a combination of the real fossil bones and castings made from other *Allosaurus* fossils. It is rare to find *Allosaurus* skeletons that are more than 50% complete, and few adult skeletons are found with their skulls fully intact. This skeleton is almost 56% complete with 139 bones recovered out of a possible 250, making Ebenezer an exceptional find.

WHERE WAS I?

> THESE **ROCK LAYERS** WERE LAID DOWN DURING THE FLOOD OF NOAH'S DAY ABOUT 4,350 YEARS AGO.

DIG SITE LOCATION

Recovered in 2001–2002, this full-grown *Allosaurus* was found in a sedimentary layer in the upper Morrison Formation within the section of the geologic column commonly labeled Jurassic. The Morrison Formation extends from Montana to New Mexico, but the dig site where Ebenezer was unearthed is near Massadona, Colorado, about 40 miles southeast of the Dinosaur Quarry in the Dinosaur National Monument.

PRE-FLOOD WORLD

Before Noah's Flood, the world bore little resemblance to present-day Colorado where Ebenezer was found. Ebenezer probably lived on a vast supercontinent[1] with a tremendous assortment of plant and animal life. We know this because the fossil record contains many more varieties of fossilized plants and animals than we see among the plants and animals living today.

DURING THE FLOOD

So, what were the final moments like for this dinosaur? During Noah's Flood, the fountains of the great deep were broken up.[2]

EBENEZER IS ONLY ONE EXAMPLE OF WHAT OCCURRED ON A GLOBAL SCALE TO **billions of creatures.**

As rain fell, water levels rose; and elevated land areas were progressively covered. Violent waves surged increasingly inland over the continental fragments where dinosaurs and other land creatures lived in the pre-Flood world. Fleeing the encroaching danger could only be a temporary reprieve as the Flood waters continued to rise and surge. The accumulating sediments quickly covered and fossilized many footprints that dinosaurs—maybe even Ebenezer—left behind.

ENTOMBED BY THE FLOOD

Overwhelmed by the rising Flood waters, Ebenezer eventually drowned as his body was swept away in a sediment debris flow consisting of a mixture of sand and pebbles. When these rapidly accumulating sediments were then deposited in this location, his body was quickly buried lying on his left side. Entombed, his bones were rapidly fossilized. Ebenezer is only one example of what occurred on a global scale to billions of creatures. Except for those on Noah's Ark, all of the dinosaurs, other land creatures, birds, and humans died in the global catastrophe.[3]

[1] As interpreted from Genesis 1:9
[2] See Genesis 7:11
[3] Genesis 7:21–23

WHAT HAPPENED TO EBENEZER?

WAIT!

SOMETHING IS MISSING!

Yes, some of Ebenezer's bones have been removed. We've taken them out of the display temporarily for research purposes.

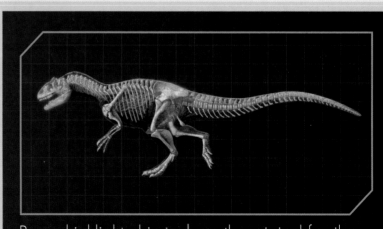

Bones highlighted in teal are the original fossils.

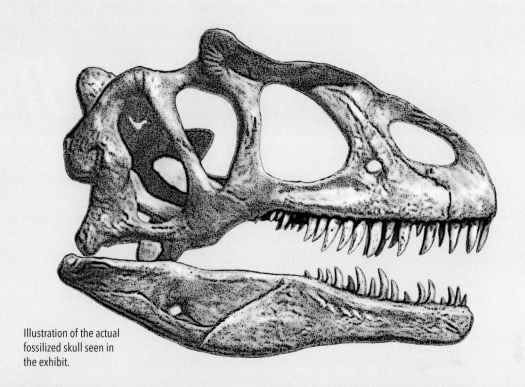

Illustration of the actual fossilized skull seen in the exhibit.

WHY THE LONG FACE ?

THIS IS THE ACTUAL FOSSILIZED **SKULL** OF EBENEZER, THE *ALLOSAURUS.*

WE CHOSE TO MOUNT THE CASTING OF THE SKULL—WHICH WEIGHS MUCH LESS—ONTO THE RESTORATION OF EBENEZER'S SKELETON. WE HAD IT PAINTED, HOWEVER, TO MATCH THE REAL FOSSIL IN ORDER TO VISUALLY REPRESENT WHAT WAS ORIGINALLY FOUND.

SKULL SPECIFICS

Notice its size. Ebenezer's skull measures 34 inches long and 22 inches high, and is 97% complete. Although this skull is slightly crushed, **IT IS ONE OF THE MOST COMPLETE *ALLOSAURUS* SKULLS EVER FOUND.** One of the reasons it is considered so complete is that the hyoid bones were found intact. The hyoid bones are part of a group of bones called the hyoid apparatus.

The hyoid apparatus served as an anchor for the muscles of the tongue as well as the larynx and helped with moving the tongue during feeding and swallowing and in vocalization. The bones of the hyoid apparatus were the only bones in the skull not touching any of the other bones in the skeleton. It "floated" between the lower jawbones, attached by ligaments and muscles.

HOLD YOUR HEAD HIGH

HEAD HAZARDS

Why is Ebenezer's real skull not displayed with the rest of his fossilized bones? Fossilized dinosaur skulls can be too heavy for a steel armature to support. If it was shown with the rest of the articulated skeleton, over time, its weight could cause the head to lower. In addition, his skull is very brittle and it is much less risky to display it in a separate case, as we have done here.

Another reason we have Ebenezer's skull mounted separately in this case, is to make it easier to remove for research purposes. The more we study this fascinating creature, the more we can learn about him and his Creator.

MOUTH MEASUREMENTS

Take a look at his immense jaws. Some scientists speculate that the jaws of an *Allosaurus* could have opened as wide as 90 degrees. Count the teeth. There are 53 curved, saw-edged, saber-like teeth, up to 4.5 inches long including the roots.

Like crocodiles and alligators, dinosaurs shed their teeth throughout their lives. The teeth that *Allosaurus* lost were replaced by others that grew in underneath the shed teeth. If you look closely at Ebenezer's upper and lower jaws, you can see teeth at various heights, showing different stages of growth.

NATURAL SELECTION
» IS NOT EVOLUTION

WHAT IS NATURAL SELECTION?

> **NATURAL SELECTION IS THE NAME CHARLES DARWIN GAVE TO AN OBSERVABLE PROCESS, WHICH RESULTS IN SMALL CHANGES IN THE PLANT AND ANIMAL WORLD, SUCH AS FUR COLOR OR PLANT HEIGHT**

A common perception popularized by many scientists is that natural selection is a primary mechanism for evolution.[1] According to the National Academy of Sciences, "Natural selection...can have radically different evolutionary effects over different time scales."[2]

Darwin believed that given enough time (millions of years) natural selection could lead to large changes (such as a dinosaur evolving into a bird) and was the underlying mechanism of unobservable molecules-to-man evolution. However, natural selection and evolution are different concepts, though today many mistakenly interchange the two.

[1] Of course, it is much more complicated than this as mutations and other proposed mechanisms are also important aspects of evolution.

[2] Science, Evolution, and Creationism, 2008, National Academies Press, Washington, D. C., p. 6.

"DARWIN'S FINCHES." Charles Darwin discovered a confusing array of plump little birds on the Galápagos Islands, but he didn't realize they were all finch species. Contrary to popular opinion, Darwin never claimed to observe natural selection on the islands.

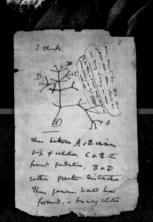

One page in a series of notebooks shows a sketch about Darwin's preliminary speculations about common descent.

DEFINING THE TERMS

Natural selection—the process by which plants or animals that possess a set of traits that have a survival advantage in a given environment pass on that advantage to their offspring (such as traits for fur color or plant height). These offspring then survive to reproduce in the next generation.

Evolution—as commonly defined today—is the idea that all life on earth has come about through descent with modification from a single-celled common ancestor. We refer to this as molecules-to-man evolution. Inherent in this process is the requirement for the origination of new genetic information as organisms evolve from simple to complex.[3]

[3] For more on the topic of information from a creation perspective see Dr. Werner Gitt's book, In the Beginning Was Information.

How does natural selection work?

Natural selection is a mechanism that allows a group of organisms of the same species (a population) to deal with changing environments. An example of this is shown in the blind cavefish exhibit. Many species possess a great diversity of genetic information for various traits, which are selected for or against. The result is a population with characteristics most favorable for a given environment with an overall loss of genetic information (diversity). These changes are non-directional (i.e., fish remain fish).[4]

Natural selection preserves the viability of a population by removing those members with severely harmful or lethal characteristics. An example of these types of characteristics is shown in the blind mice exhibit.

Although natural selection results in the death of some organisms, it exhibits the care of God for His creation through a mechanism that preserves populations of organisms in a sin-cursed, post-Fall world.

[4] For more on the topic of natural selection from a creation perspective see "Is Natural Selection the Same Thing as Evolution?" in The New Answers Book.

COMMON MISCONCEPTIONS

**ABOUT NATURAL SELECTION.
THE REAL PROBLEM WITH EQUATING EVOLUTION AND NATURAL SELECTION IS THAT NATURAL SELECTION IS NOT CAPABLE OF MEETING THE REQUIREMENTS FOR EVOLUTION.**

Results of Natural Selection	Required by Evolution
• Decrease genetic information (diversity).	• Increase or provide new genetic information.
• Allow organisms to survive better in a given environment (non-directional).	• Allow organisms to progress from molecules to man (directional).
• Consistent with creation's "orchard."	• Consistent with evolution's "tree" of life.

Evolution's "Tree" and Creation's "Orchard"

The evolution "tree"—based on man's opinion—postulates that all past and present animals descended from one common, single-celled ancestor over millions of years. The "tree" assumes kinds of animals evolve into other kinds (such as dinosaurs into birds).

The creation "orchard"—based on the Bible—shows that God created different kinds of animals during the creation week and these have diversified within their kinds (such as the original dog kind diversified into coyotes, foxes, domestic dogs) over a few thousand years leading to all past and present animals.

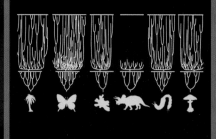

>BLIND CAVEFISH

PROOF OF EVOLUTION?

Mexican tetras *(Astyanax mexicanus)* come in two basic forms:
- An albino (no pigmentation) without eyes that dwells in caves, known simply as "blind cavefish."
- A sighted form with eyes and pigmented skin that lives on the surface.

Both are considered the same species because they will readily produce offspring with each other.

Cavefish may be blind and lack pigmentation for several reasons:
- One possibility is that cavefish accumulate harmful mutations in genes important for eye development. These mutations are not selected against in a cave because the fish do not need eyes to see food in the dark. On the other hand, blindness would be selected against in a lighted environment (which is why the sighted form is found on the surface).

- The dark environment may also be the reason cavefish lack pigmentation for skin color. In the dark they do not need the protection that pigmentation affords to those living on the surface, so mutations that result in a loss of pigmentation are not selected against in the cave.

- Another possibility is that cavefish with no eyes may be selected for in a cave because the same mutations that lead to loss of eye development also lead to increased ability to taste and perceive their surroundings. This would be beneficial in a dark environment when a fish is searching for food.

Although these fish are often viewed as an "icon of evolution," they instead represent fish that are very well adapted for the cave environment thanks to the combined effects of mutations and natural selection. These processes have led to a decrease in genetic information (loss of eyes and pigmentation) not an increase as required for molecules-to-man evolution.

After Noah's Flood, the world was very different, having many new environments, like caves, which might not have existed to any great extent in the pre-Flood world that perished. Original created variability, or in some instances, variability due to mutations, allowed plants and animals, including fish, to quickly colonize these new environments.

WHAT ABOUT SPECIATION WITHIN KINDS?

Natural selection and artificial selection (performed by man) acting on variation in a given population and environment may result in multiple "species" (a man-made term). Contrary to evolutionary ideas, speciation has never resulted in one kind of organism evolving into another kind, such as a reptile evolving into a bird. After the Flood, natural selection (among other mechanisms) likely resulted in speciation as the animal kinds adapted to the many new post-Flood environments.

Variation in Darwin's finches

Although often viewed as an icon of evolution, Darwin's finches serve as a perfect model of variation within a created kind.

In Genesis 1:21 we learn that God created "every winged bird according to its kind." Baraminologists (scientists who study created kinds) have determined that "kind" is typically equivalent to the "family" level (in relation to common classification terminology). All of Darwin's finches belong to the same family, Emberizidae, and therefore likely belong to the same created kind (other families of birds may also belong to this kind).

Natural selection (in addition to other mechanisms) acting in different environments, such as varying weather, food sources, and competitors on the Galápagos Islands where the finches reside, has caused fluctuations in the populations of finches and possibly led to finch speciation but never a finch evolving into another kind of organism. What we observe is the selection of existing genetic information for beak size and other characteristics, not the addition of new genetic information as required for molecules-to-man evolution.

The finches in this exhibit are taxidermist reproductions and not actual specimens of Darwin's finches.

Dire wolf (extinct)

Coyote

English bulldog

Chihuahua

Variation within the dog kind

Two types of selection—natural and artificial— are the primary mechanisms that have led to the many different types of dogs that exist today.

It has been determined genetically that all dogs (wolves, coyotes, foxes, jackals, dingoes, and domestic dogs) are related to each other.[6,7]

- Natural selection (and other mechanisms) has likely resulted in the different species of dogs found in the wild, such as the dire wolf and coyote.

- Artificial selection (carried out through breeding programs designed by humans) has resulted in many of the domestic dog breeds, such as the English bulldog and Chihuahua.

In Genesis 1:24 God said, "Let the earth bring forth the living creature according to its kind: cattle and creeping thing and beast of the earth, each according to its kind" (dogs were likely in the category of beast of the earth). All dogs, whether wild or domestic, belong to the same family— Canidae. Thus, all dogs likely belong to the same created kind.

Natural and artificial selection have acted upon variation within the populations of dogs leading to the wide variety of dogs we see today. Dogs have never evolved into another kind of organism. Instead, what we observe is the selection of existing genetic information for head shape, length of fur, overall size, and other characteristics, not the addition of new genetic information as required for molecules-to-man evolution.

[6] Carles Vilà, et al. (1997). "Multiple and Ancient Origins of the Domestic Dog." *Science* 276:1687–1689.

[7] Kerstin Lindblad-Toh, et al. (2005). "Genome sequence, comparative analysis, and haplotype structure of the domestic dog," *Nature* 438:803–819.

ANTIBIOTIC RESISTANCE

⟩ "EVOLUTION IN ACTION" OR NOT?

Antibiotic resistance in bacteria is commonly used as an example of "evolution in action." But are the bacteria really evolving?

Antibiotics interact with a protein in normal bacteria and prevent it from functioning properly, killing the bacteria (**PANEL A**). Antibiotic-resistant bacteria produce a mutant form of that protein.[5] The antibiotic cannot interact with the mutant protein and the mutant bacteria live (**PANEL B**). However, this comes at a cost. The mutant bacteria are less "fit" than the normal bacteria and may be at a disadvantage in other environments (for example, when the antibiotic is removed— **PANEL C**).

Using the points previously discussed:

- Genetic information was lost through mutation. No new information was added.
- Antibiotic resistant bacteria are less "fit" overall (non-directional).
- Variation has occurred within the bacterial population.

Antibiotic resistance in bacteria is a compelling example of natural selection in action, not "evolution in action."

[5] Antibiotic resistance can be gained in multiple ways.

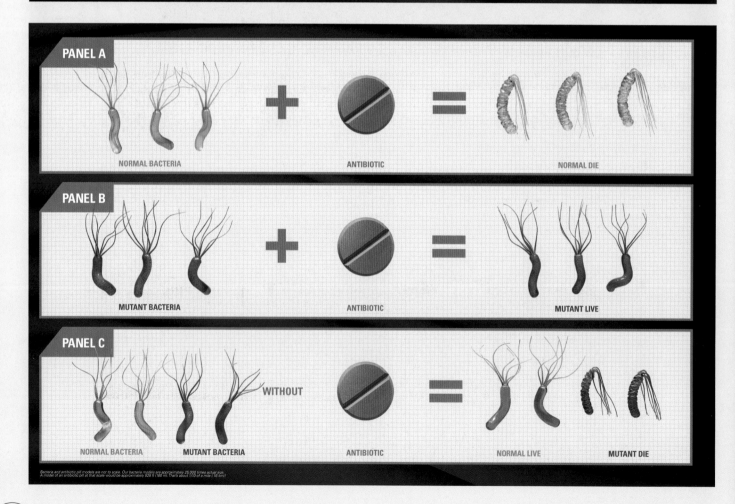

PANEL A — NORMAL BACTERIA + ANTIBIOTIC = NORMAL DIE

PANEL B — MUTANT BACTERIA + ANTIBIOTIC = MUTANT LIVE

PANEL C — NORMAL BACTERIA / MUTANT BACTERIA WITHOUT ANTIBIOTIC = NORMAL LIVE / MUTANT DIE

Bacteria and antibiotic pill models are not to scale. Our bacteria models are approximately 25,000 times actual size. A model of an antibiotic pill at that scale would be approximately 528 ft (160 m). That's about 1/10 of a mile (.16 km).

>THREE BLIND MICE
MUTATIONS = LOSS OF INFORMATION

The mutant mice have a small deletion in one gene in their DNA that results in the formation of a defective protein named MITF-*mi*. Unless they receive intervening care, these mice die shortly after weaning because they do not have teeth and cannot chew food. A related disorder can be found in humans called Waardenburg syndrome.

The following is a list of the problems that occur in the mutant mice:

- Deafness
- Blindness
- No visible teeth
- No fur pigmentation (albino)
- Deficient immune system
- Abnormal bones

The mutant mice would be selected against and not survive in the wild. This would eliminate the mutated genes and preserve the viability of the rest of the population.

The mice in this exhibit are taxidermist reproductions and not actual specimens of mutant *mi/mi* mice.

CONCLUSION

> Natural selection is an observable process that occurs in the present. What this process is capable of doing and has done in the past comes down to this:

Do we view natural selection using God's Word or man's opinion as our foundation?

Natural selection is supported biblically and scientifically. It can be viewed as a God-ordained process that allows organisms to survive in a post-Fall world. Natural selection cannot (despite the common perception) be the mechanism for molecules-to-man evolution since it does not have the ability to create new genetic information (mutations cannot do this either). Natural selection allows limited variation within populations, preserves the viability of populations, and is, in fact, a great confirmation of the Bible's history.

THE WORLD DRIES

⟩ THE CONTINENTS DRY AFTER THE FLOOD

Lake system above Kaibab Upwarp

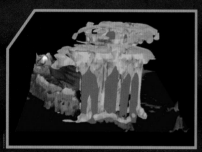

Hypercane computer simulation

During the Flood, volcanic activity warmed the oceans. Models suggest that warm oceans generated high rainfall, which created huge lakes all over the world, such as the lakes above Grand Canyon.

Models also suggest that the warm oceans created hypercanes—continent-sized hurricanes which lasted for centuries. Jupiter's Great Red Spot is a hypercane, which has persisted more than three centuries.

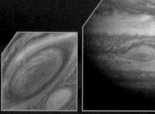

Jupiter's Great Red Spot

As evaporation cooled the oceans in the centuries following the Flood, the earth gradually cooled and dried.

Cooling of oceans after the Flood
(δO^{18} in foraminifera)

LIFE RECOVERS

> GO OUT OF THE ARK...AND BRING EVERY LIVING THING THAT IS WITH YOU...THAT THEY MAY BREED ABUNDANTLY IN THE EARTH, AND BE FRUITFUL AND MULTIPLY UPON THE EARTH. (GENESIS 8:16–17)

ORGANISMS CHANGE RAPIDLY AS THE EARTH CHANGES

As North America cooled and dried following the Flood

- larger species replaced smaller species
- grass-eating species replaced leaf-eating species
- swift species of the open plain replaced slower species

ARK EQUID
HUMID FORESTS

PLIOHIPPUS   MERYCHIPPUS   MIOHIPPUS   MODERN EQUID
DRY GRASSLANDS

Present changes are too small and too slow to explain these differences, suggesting God provided organisms with special tools to change rapidly.

VARIETY RECOVERS RAPIDLY AFTER THE FLOOD

Two of each kind of land animal (and more of the clean animals) were represented on the Ark. Other species in each kind appeared rapidly after the Flood. The Creator built this variety into the original organisms at the creation.

Present Species

Ark Kind
TYPICAL MAMMAL KIND

Present Species

Survivor of the Flood
TYPICAL PLANT KIND

In the last few centuries, hundreds of domesticated dog varieties were bred, suggesting incredible variety is built into organisms.

The dogs leaving the Ark generated all the dog species in the present, including coyotes, wolves, and foxes.

PAIR OF CANIDS ON THE ARK

cross of
Brassavola, Laelia,
and Cattleya

cross of
Brassavola and Cattleya

cross of
Doritis and
Phalaenopsis

cross of
Sophronitis, Laelia,
and Cattleya

cross of
Broughtonia and Cattleya

cross of
Brassavola and Laelia

cross of
Laelia and Cattleya

cross of
Vuylstekeara and
Oncidium

Hybridization is common within families of many plants and animals, suggesting they arose recently from a common ancestor.

MARSUPIALS

Marsupials, which have pouches, can nurse their young while moving. That may explain why on each continent marsupials were the first mammals buried and preserved after the Flood.

Placental mammals, which must stop to nurse their young, spread out more slowly, gradually dominating in Eurasia, Africa, North America, and finally South America.

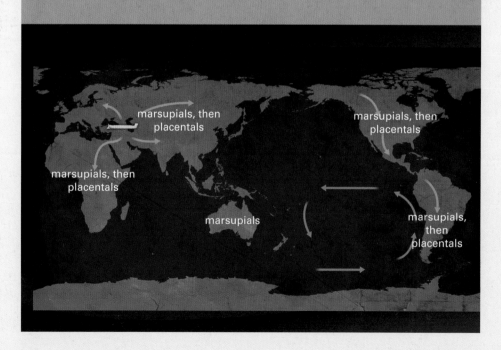

marsupials, then placentals

marsupials, then placentals

marsupials, then placentals

marsupials

marsupials, then placentals

LIFE REFILLS THE EARTH
ORGANISMS SPREAD ACROSS CONTINENTS RAPIDLY AFTER THE FLOOD

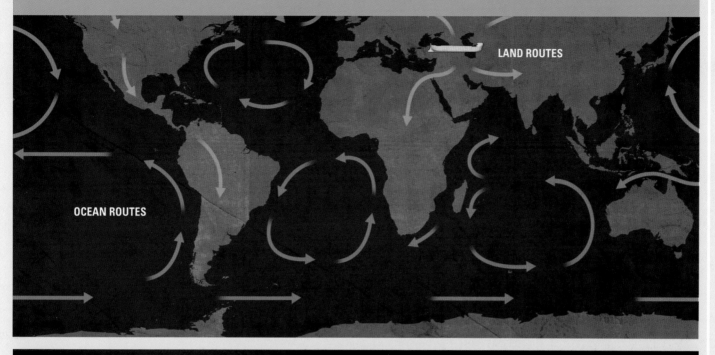

LAND ROUTES

OCEAN ROUTES

RAFTING

> WHEN THE FLOOD DESTROYED THE WORLD'S FORESTS, IT MUST HAVE LEFT BILLIONS OF TREES FLOAT-
> ING FOR CENTURIES ON THE OCEAN. THESE LOG MATS SERVED AS READY MADE RAFTS FOR ANIMALS
> TO CROSS OCEANS. THE PATHS OF OCEANS CURRENTS, CARRYING THESE RAFTS, WOULD EXPLAIN:

similar animals and plants on opposite sides of oceans

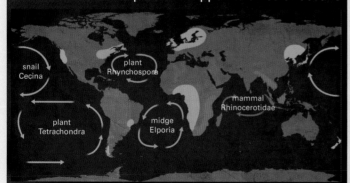

places of high diversity (probable landing sites)

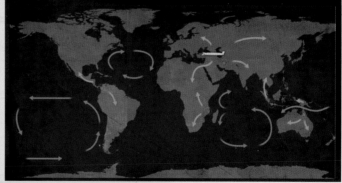

distribution of Geochelone tortoises

THE WORLD CHILLS

> ### CONTINENTS COOL RAPIDLY AFTER THE FLOOD

Within a few centuries of the Flood, it cooled enough for rain to fall as snow. In what is often called the Ice Age, great ice sheets formed on the continents.

ICE CORES

Ice in the middle of Greenland and Antarctica is miles thick. But currently, snow falls only near the ocean. So, modern processes did not build up the earth's ice sheets.

Mammoth

Cave Bear

WOOLLY GIANTS

Frozen carcasses of bears, mammoths, and rhinoceroses are found in North America and Siberia. Their heavy wool and size suggest a climate unlike the present. Their unusual burial suggests catastrophic conditions unlike anything we see today.

THE LAND RECOVERS
)THE CRUST SETTLES DOWN AFTER THE FLOOD

Even today, the Grand Tetons rise while Jackson Hole sinks.

The Flood moved continents, rocks, and sediment on a global scale. Thick crust at the end of the Flood needed time to sink to the proper level, and thin crust needed time to thicken.

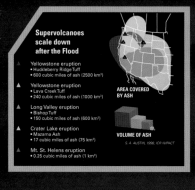

Supervolcanoes scale down after the Flood

Yellowstone eruption
• Huckleberry Ridge Tuff
• 600 cubic miles of ash (2500 km³)

Yellowstone eruption
• Lava Creek Tuff
• 240 cubic miles of ash (1000 km³)

Long Valley eruption
• Bishop Tuff
• 150 cubic miles of ash (600 km³)

Crater Lake eruption
• Mazama Ash
• 17 cubic miles of ash (75 km³)

Mt. St. Helens eruption
• 0.25 cubic miles of ash (1 km³)

AREA COVERED BY ASH

VOLUME OF ASH
S. A. AUSTIN, 1998, ICR IMPACT

The motion of the crust generated catastrophes, large at first, smaller in time. Supervolcanoes and superquakes rocked the earth for centuries, gradually diminishing in size and frequency to the quakes and volcanoes we have today.

Rhino preserved in ash from a supervolcano

While organisms refilled the earth and changed rapidly with the climate, catastrophes buried them, preserving a record of these turbulent times.

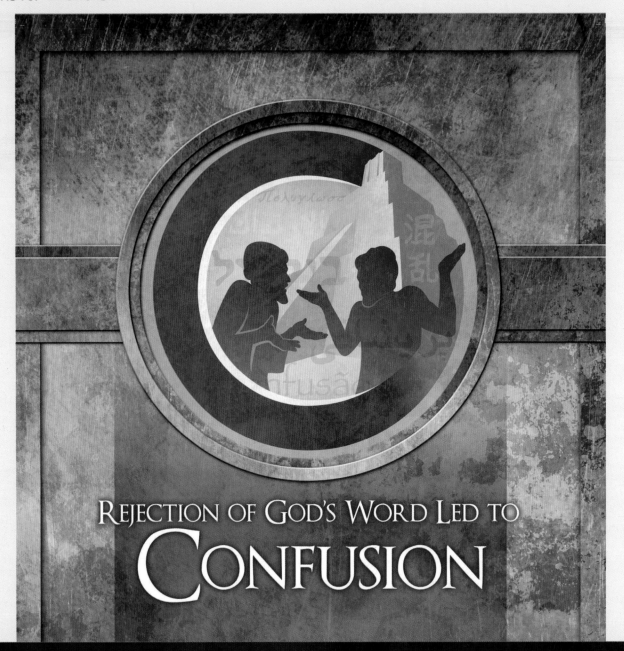

REJECTION OF GOD'S WORD LED TO
CONFUSION

When Noah's descendants disobeyed God's command to fill the earth,
God gave them different languages, causing them to spread over the earth.
The scattering of people explains the formation of different people groups.

CREATION CORRUPTION CATASTROPHE CONFUSION CHRIST CROSS CONSUMMATION

The Lord confounded the language of all the earth and . . . scattered them abroad. *Genesis 11:9*

GOD SCATTERS THE NATIONS

It came to pass that they found a plain in the land of Shinar; and they dwelt there.

And they said, "Come, let us build ourselves a city and a tower, whose top may reach to heaven; and come, let us make ourselves a name, lest we be scattered abroad upon the face of the whole earth."

And the Lord said, "Behold, the people is one, and they all have one language; and this they begin to do. Let us go down, and there confuse their language, that they may not understand one another's speech."

So the Lord scattered them abroad from there upon the face of all the earth: and they left off building the city.

Genesis 11:1–9

THE ENTRANCE OF HUMAN RELIGION

At Babel, humans rejected God's plan, worshipping the creation rather than the Creator and following their own way rather than God's way. All human religions have followed their example, inventing myths to replace God's account of creation and Noah's Flood. They ignore God's warnings of judgment and His promises of blessing.

THE REBUILDING OF CIVILIZATION

The Flood destroyed civilization and rearranged the whole surface of the earth. While forests regrew and resources were rediscovered, humans made do with whatever shelters they could find and materials they could easily fashion.

Human remains found around the world (including those named *Homo erectus*, Neanderthal, and Cro-Magnon) show that the immigrants from Babel found shelter in newly formed caves and made tools out of rocks and sticks to meet basic needs. They left behind artifacts, musical instruments, ceremonial burials, and fire pits, which show that they were intelligent and fully human.

Fragment of a flute apparently made by a Neanderthal discovered in a cave of the Idrijca valley, Western Slovenia, 1996

Within the lifetime of Noah and his sons, the families who left Babel began rediscovering resources and using the knowledge from pre-Flood times to quickly build remarkable civilizations.

According to HUMAN REASON...

EVERYONE DECIDES WHAT IS RIGHT IN HIS OWN EYES

"Every man did that which was right in his own eyes." **Judges 21:25**

Once people abandon the authority of God's Word, there is no sure foundation for morality and justice in the world. Human reason can be used to justify evil of every sort.

RACISM

GENOCIDE

Rather than embracing our neighbors, we exterminate them.

Rather than esteeming our brothers, we discriminate against them.

Rather than protecting our brothers, we hate them.

"Biological arguments for racism may have been common before 1859, but they increased by orders of magnitude following the acceptance of evolutionary theory."

—Stephen Jay Gould, a leading evolutionist, explaining how people in the nineteenth century abused science to support their own prejudices (*Ontogeny and Phylogeny*, 1977).

RECENT EXCUSES TO REJECT GOD'S WORD...
EVOLUTION OVER MILLIONS OF YEARS

ABORTION

NO CHOICE FOR THEM
46,000,000 babies killed since Roe v. Wade 1/22/73
Before I formed thee in the belly I knew thee ...
Jer 1:5

Rather than protecting the helpless, we murder them.

Without any absolute authority for right and wrong, humans in every generation have devised a multitude of excuses to justify abuse. Modern humans are no different. They have abused science to justify all sorts of evils. According to evolution, humans are nothing special:

- We have no Creator and are not accountable to anyone.
- Hominids evolved into many branches over millions of years.
- Death is a natural step in the cycle of life.
- We're just animals, and the fittest survive.

WHO'S YOUR BROTHER?

"God has made of one blood all nations." Acts 17:26

GOD'S WORD AGREES WITH GOD'S WORLD...

WE'RE ALL ONE BLOOD

"Of the three sons of Noah the whole earth was overspread." **Genesis 9:19**

The Horder twins show that from the same parents, one girl inherited genes for a large amount of melanin and the other girl inherited genes for a small amount of melanin.

God's Word says that all people after the Flood descended from Noah's three sons. When the events of the Tower of Babel split up the human gene pool, different combinations of genes in different groups resulted in some people having predominantly light skin and some having predominantly dark skin, as well as shades in between.

Every human being has the same basic brown pigment called melanin in the skin. Combinations of genes determine how much or how little melanin each person has.

In just a few generations, different combinations of previously existing genetic information resulted in distinct people groups with superficial differences, such as different skin tones and eye shapes. Modern science recognizes that our differences are superficial.

BIOLOGICAL DIFFERENCES ARE SUPERFICIAL

If Adam and Eve were middle brown, their children could have exhibited the whole range of skin tones from light to dark.

Our superficial differences are merely the result of different combinations of features that humans had since the creation. The variety among different people groups could have occurred very recently and quickly in small populations in only a few generations.

WE CAME FROM ONE WOMAN

"Eve was the mother of all living." **Genesis 3:20**

We know from God's Word that all people descended from one woman, Eve. Mitochondrial DNA is passed directly from mother to child. We would predict that mitochondrial DNA would be similar in all people alive today. Scientific research on mitochondrial DNA seems to bear this out.

WE CAME FROM ONE MAN

"The first man [was] Adam." **I Corinthians 15:45**

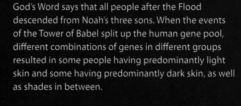

Mitochondrial DNA

We know from God's Word that all people descended from one man, Adam. The Y-chromosome contains DNA that is passed directly from father to son. We would predict that Y-chromosome DNA would be similar in all men alive today. Scientific research on Y-chromosome DNA seems to bear this out.

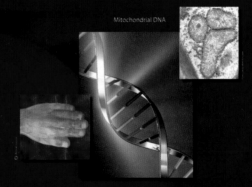

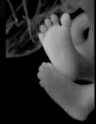

WE ARE FULLY HUMAN FROM CONCEPTION

All the genetic information unique to humans is present at conception. So right from the start a fertilized human egg cell is totally human. There is no biological basis for drawing any other line for when we "become" human. Every human is fully human, from conception to the end of life.

ACCORDING TO GOD'S WORD...

WE'RE ALL ONE RACE - "ONE BLOOD"

"God has made of one blood all nations." **Acts 17:26**

Six thousand years ago, God created a perfect world and fashioned the first two humans in His image. Humans were created to rule under God and to care for all of God's creation. After the Flood, God restated this plan to Noah and his three sons.

According to God's Word, all the people on earth today descended from Noah's three sons, who descended from the first man Adam. So we all share the same blood line. We're all brothers.

WE'RE ALL CREATED BY GOD
"God formed man of the dust of the ground." **Genesis 2:7**

WE'RE ALL IN GOD'S IMAGE
God said, "Let us make man in our image." **Genesis 1:26**

WE'RE ALL ONE FAMILY
"God has made of one blood all nations." **Acts 17:26**

WE'RE ALL LOVED BY GOD
"God so loved the world that He gave His only begotten Son." **John 3:16**

GOD'S WORD CONDEMNS THE ABUSE OF OTHERS

God said to Noah and his sons, *"The life of the flesh is the blood thereof. At the hand of every man's brother I will require the life of man. Whoever sheds man's blood, his blood shall be shed by man: for in the image of God he made man"* (Genesis 9:4–6).

After destroying the pre-Flood world because of rampant violence, God instituted governments to judge violence of brother against brother. According to God, abuse of others is a sin against the Creator, who made every human being in His image. In the case of murder, the just punishment is the shedding of blood.

God's Word condemns a long list of abuses: the abuse of the unborn, the abuse of the young, the abuse of the old, the sick, and the poor. Principles derived from God's Word also condemn discrimination based on language, culture, gender, or skin tone.

BABEL EXPLAINS

"Of the three sons of Noah the whole earth was overspread" **Genesis 9:19**

BLACK SEA

MAGOG

ROME

DESCENDANTS OF JAPHETH

JAVAN

TIRAS

GREECE

MEDITERRANEAN SEA

CANA

EGYPT

MIZRAIM

Different Languages

At Babel, God created numerous languages. Over time, these languages changed into the thousands of different languages we have today. Yet modern languages still follow patterns of the original languages at Babel.

DESCENDANTS OF HAM

CUSH

"By the sons of Noah were the nations divided" **Genesis 10:32**

OUR DIFFERENCES

GOMER

CASPIAN SEA

ASSHUR

MADAI

ASSYRIA

DESCENDANTS OF SHEM

BABYLON

ELAM

PERSIA

PERSIAN GULF

ARABIAN DESERT

JOKTAN

Different Nations

All the humans who settled the earth after the Flood descended from Noah's three sons. Yet the human gene pool split up after Babel. In just a few generations, different combinations of previously existing genetic information resulted in distinct people groups, each with superficial differences, including different skin tones and eye shapes.

"God has made of one blood all nations" Acts 17:26

GOD'S PROMISE

God judged the disobedience
of Adam and Eve.
You shall return to dust.
Genesis 3:19

God judged mankind's
rebellion at Babel.
*The Lord did confuse the
languages of all the earth.*
Genesis 11:4

JUDGMENT OF NATIONS

Mankind's disobedience did not end at Babel.
Since then, God has continued to judge the
wickedness of nations, often raising up other
nations to humble them. Prophecy after
prophecy has been fulfilled. God always
keeps His word.

God judged the wickedness of
Noah's generation.
*I do bring a flood of waters upon
the earth, to destroy all flesh.*
Genesis 6:17

FIRST FAMILY — NOAH'S WORLD — BABEL — EGYPT

God assured Noah and His
sons that He would never
again destroy the earth in a
worldwide Flood.
*Never again shall there be a
flood to destroy the earth.*
Genesis 9:11

God sent
Joseph to save
Egypt from
coming famine
*The famine
was in all
lands, but in
the land of
Egypt there
was bread.*
**Genesis
41:54**

BLESSING OF NATIONS

God's judgments are often attended by promises of
great blessing. When Adam sinned in the Garden, for
example, God promised
a Seed who would crush
the serpent. After judging
mankind at Babel, God
chose to bless all nations
through the Seed of Abra-
ham. God has always kept
His promises.

God provided a covering
for mankind's sins.
*God made coats of skins,
and clothed Adam and Eve.*
Genesis 3:21

God promised to bless
Abraham and make him the
father of the Hebrew nation.
*I will make of you a great
nation, and I will bless you.*
Genesis 12:2-3

God promised to preserve the
Seed through Abraham's only son.
*Take your only son . . . . and
in your seed shall all the
nations of the earth be blessed.*
Genesis 22:2, 18

GOD'S SEED
PROMISED TO THE NATIONS

God promised Eve a Seed that
would crush the serpent's head.
Her seed shall bruise your head.
Genesis 3:15

Adam ... Noah ... Abraham

Throughout history, God has preserved the Seed promised to Adam and Eve.
God's prophets also revealed more and more details about the Seed. They
said this child, or "Seed," would be a deliverer, a uniquely born son, a prophet,
an eternal priest, and an everlasting king. But he would be "cut off."

God promised to preserve the
Seed through Noah.
*With you and your seed will
I establish my covenant, . . .
and you shall come into the
ark.* **Genesis 6:18 & 9:9**

God promised that the
Seed would be a prophet.
*God will raise up a
Prophet from
among your brothers, like
you.* **Deuteronomy 18:18**

TO THE NATIONS

God said to Abraham, "In your seed shall all the nations of the earth be blessed." **Genesis 22:18**

God used Assyria to judge other nations.
Have you not heard how I brought it to pass, that you should lay waste fenced cities into ruinous heaps?
2 Kings 19:25

God judged Pharaoh for refusing to free the Hebrew people.
I will send all my plagues upon your people, so that you may know that there is none like me on the earth.
Exodus 9:14

God used Babylon to judge other nations.
I have given all these lands into the hand of Nebuchadnezzar the king of Babylon, my servant; and all nations shall serve him.
Jeremiah 27:6

God prophesied that Persia would judge other nations.
The Lord says to his anointed, to Cyrus, whose right hand I have held, to subdue nations, I will go before you, though you have not known me.
Isaiah 45:1

God prophesied that Greece would judge other nations.
A kingdom of brass shall bear rule over all the earth.
Daniel 2:39

God prophesied that Rome would judge other nations.
The kingdom shall be strong as iron: forasmuch as iron breaks in pieces and subdues all things.
Daniel 2:40

ASSYRIA ——— BABYLON ——— PERSIA ——— GREECE ——— ROME

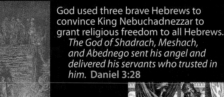

God used three brave Hebrews to convince King Nebuchadnezzar to grant religious freedom to all Hebrews.
The God of Shadrach, Meshach, and Abednego sent his angel and delivered his servants who trusted in him. Daniel 3:28

As God prophesied, the Hebrews won independence from a wicked king who tried to desecrate the temple of God.
The people that know their God shall be strong and do exploits.
Daniel 11:33

God sent Jonah to save Assyria's capital city from coming destruction.
So the people of Nineveh believed God ... and God saw that they turned from their evil way, and God repented of the evil that he said that he would do to them. Jonah 3:5, 10

God used Queen Esther to save the Hebrews from a plot to wipe them out.
*There was great fasting....
Then Mordecai answered Esther, "Deliverance shall arise to the Jews."*
Esther 4:3, 14

As God prophesied, a messenger came and prepared the way for the Seed to bless all nations.
Behold, I will send my messenger, and he shall prepare the way before me: and the Lord, whom you seek, shall suddenly come to his temple.
Malachi 3:1

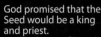

God promised that the Seed would be a king and priest.
The throne of David shall be established forever. 1 Kings 2:45
You are a priest forever. Psalm 110:4

God promised that the Seed would be killed.
After sixty and two weeks the Messiah shall be cut off. Daniel 9:26

God promised that the Seed would be the mighty God.
For a child is born to us, and his name shall be called Wonderful, Counselor, the mighty God, the everlasting Father, the Prince of Peace.
Isaiah 9:6

Christ, Cross, Consummation

Christ

Cross

Consummation

Old Testament Prophecy

After the dispersion at Babel, God spoke through Israel's prophets, revealing details of His plan to redeem His creation.

God Himself would be the Savior we needed.

These prophecies describe precise facts about the birth, life, ministry, Crucifixion, and Resurrection of the Savior.

Birth *of* the Savior

The Old Testament revealed that the Savior would be:

Born of a virgin *Isaiah 7:14*

in the town of Bethlehem *Micah 5:2*

and that He would be
a descendant of Abraham *Genesis 12:1–3*

through Isaac *Genesis 17:19*

and Jacob *Genesis 28:14*

in the line of Judah *Genesis 49:10*

and the house of David *2 Samuel 7:12–13*

Ministry of the Savior

The prophets stated that the Savior would be:

An obedient Prophet *Deuteronomy 18:18*

A faithful Priest *1 Samuel 2:35*

The eternal King *Isaiah 9:6*

"God with us" *Isaiah 7:14*

A healer of the deaf, blind, sick, and diseased *Isaiah 35:5, 53:4*

A great light in Galilee *Isaiah 9:1-2*

A parable teller *Psalm 78:2*

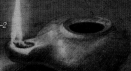

Response to the Savior

The Old Testament foretold that the Savior would:

Enter Jerusalem on a colt, the foal of a donkey *Zechariah 9:9*

Be hailed as the long-awaited Messiah *Psalm 118:26*

Be rejected by His people *Psalm 118:22*

Betrayed by a friend *Psalm 41:9*

For 30 pieces of silver *Zechariah 11:12*

Be severely beaten *Isaiah 52:14, 53:5*

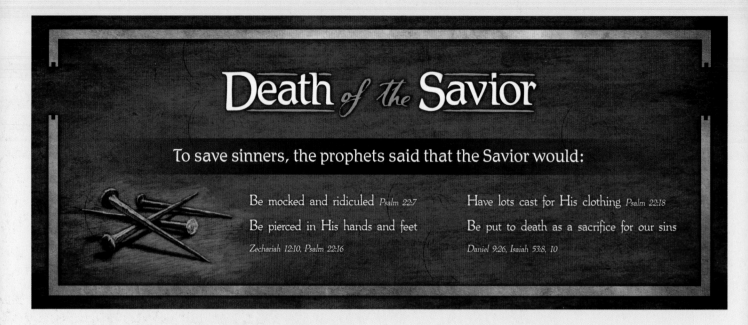

Death *of the* Savior

To save sinners, the prophets said that the Savior would:

Be mocked and ridiculed *Psalm 22:7*

Be pierced in His hands and feet
Zechariah 12:10, Psalm 22:16

Have lots cast for His clothing *Psalm 22:18*

Be put to death as a sacrifice for our sins
Daniel 9:26, Isaiah 53:8, 10

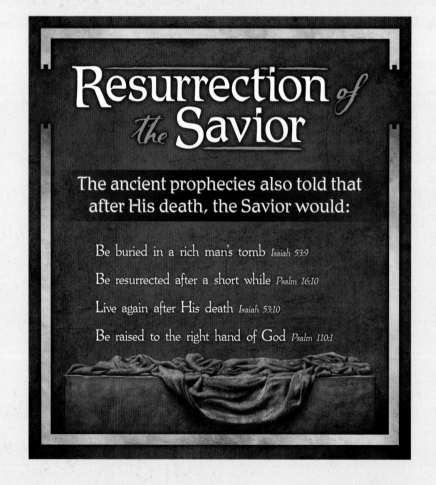

Resurrection *of the* Savior

The ancient prophecies also told that after His death, the Savior would:

Be buried in a rich man's tomb *Isaiah 53:9*

Be resurrected after a short while *Psalm 16:10*

Live again after His death *Isaiah 53:10*

Be raised to the right hand of God *Psalm 110:1*

Son of God

The angel said to Mary,
"The Holy Spirit will come upon you, and the power of
the Most High will overshadow you, and for that reason
the holy Child will be called the Son of God."

Luke 1:35

Joseph and his
betrothed wife,
Mary, a virgin,
traveled to
Bethlehem to
register for
the census called by
Caesar Augustus.
While they were
there, she gave
birth to her
firstborn son,
wrapped Him in
swaddling cloths,
and laid Him in
a manger.

Luke 2:1–7

Announcement to the Shepherds

Nearby, shepherds kept watch over the flocks at night.
An angel of the Lord appeared and said, "I bring you
good news of great joy for all people. A Savior was born
today in the city of David. He is Christ the Lord."
And suddenly there was a multitude of
angels praising God. "Glory to God in the highest,
And on earth peace, goodwill toward men!"

Luke 2:8–14

Immanuel

So all this was done that it might be fulfilled which was spoken by the Lord through the prophet, saying: "Behold, the virgin shall be with child, and bear a Son, and they shall call His name Immanuel," which is translated, "God with us."

Matthew 1:22–23

Christians believe that Jesus is fully God and fully man, the Son of God, and the second Person of the Trinity.

Other religions distort these teachings. Mormons and Jehovah's Witnesses portray Jesus as a created being instead of the infinite Creator, and Muslims claim that Jesus was merely a prophet.

Secularists often present Jesus as being overly gentle and never judgmental. They may accept that He was a good moral teacher but certainly not God in the flesh.

But what does the Bible teach? What did Jesus say about Himself?

Jesus *is* God

Jesus applied God's name to Himself:

Jesus said to them, "Most assuredly, I say to you, before Abraham was, I AM." *John 8:58–59*

Jesus said that He grants eternal life and claimed equality with God the Father:

"My sheep hear My voice...and I give them eternal life. I and My Father are one." *John 10:30*

Jesus said He had authority to forgive sins:

When Jesus saw their faith, He said to the paralytic, "Son, your sins are forgiven." *Mark 2:5*

Jesus is the Creator

Jesus, the Word, was with God in the beginning

In the beginning was the Word, and the Word was with God, and the Word was God...All things were made through Him, and without Him nothing was made that was made.

John 1:1, 3

Jesus created all things

For by Him all things were created that are in heaven and that are on earth, visible and invisible... All things were created through Him and for Him. And He is before all things, and in Him all things consist.

Colossians 1:16–17

Jesus made the world

God has in these last days spoken to us by His Son, whom He has appointed heir of all things, through whom also He made everything.

Hebrews 1:2

I AM

the Bread of Life

He who comes to Me shall never hunger,
and he who believes in Me shall never thirst. *John 6:35*

the Light of the World

He who follows Me shall not walk in darkness,
but have the light of life. *John 8:12*

the Door

If anyone enters by Me, he will be saved,
and will go in and out and find pasture. *John 10:9*

the Good Shepherd

The good shepherd gives his life for the sheep. *John 10:11*

the Resurrection and the Life

He who believes in Me, though he may die, he shall live.
And whoever lives and believes in Me shall never die. *John 11:25-26*

the Way, the Truth, and the Life

No one comes to the Father except through Me. *John 14:6*

the Vine

He who abides in Me, and I in him, bears much fruit;
for without Me you can do nothing. *John 15:5*

Jesus *and* Genesis

Many Christians have been taught that it is not important to understand Genesis 1–11 as accurately describing real history. But how did Jesus Christ view these chapters?

Jesus called Abel a righteous man and talked about him as being the first person to be murdered. *Matthew 23:35*

While discussing marriage and divorce, Jesus quoted from Genesis 1 and 2, affirming that Adam and Eve were real people created at the beginning. *Mark 10:6–7*

Jesus taught people that Noah entered the Ark and was spared from the Flood that killed everyone outside the Ark. *Luke 17:27*

Jesus treated these chapters as being historically accurate, describing real people and events. Since He is the Creator and existed when these people were alive and these events occurred, we should trust what He said.

Teachings *of* Jesus

Jesus taught His followers how they should live. He explained how people should treat one another and warned about the consequences of rejecting Him. The following list is a small representation of His teachings from Matthew's Gospel.

⟨ Instructions ⟩

Love the Lord your God with all your heart, with all your soul, and with all your mind. *Matthew 22:37*

Love your enemies. *Matthew 5:44*

Make disciples of all nations. *Matthew 28:19*

Blessed are those who are persecuted for righteousness' sake. *Matthew 5:10*

You are the light of the world. *Matthew 5:14*

No one can serve two masters. *Matthew 6:24*

Beware of false prophets who come to you in sheep's clothing. *Matthew 7:15*

⟨ Rebukes ⟩

Then I will say to them, "I never knew you; depart from Me, you workers of lawlessness." *Matthew 7:23*

Woe to you, scribes and Pharisees, hypocrites! You are like whitewashed tombs that appear beautiful on the outside, but are full of dead men's bones and all uncleanness. *Matthew 23:27*

Serpents, brood of vipers! How can you escape the condemnation of hell? *Matthew 23:33*

Depart from Me, you cursed, into the everlasting fire prepared for the devil and his angels. *Matthew 25:41*

Look, we are going up to Jerusalem. The Son of Man will be betrayed to the chief priests and to the scribes, and they will condemn Him to death and deliver Him to the Gentiles to mock, scourge, and crucify. And on the third day He will be raised. *Matthew 20:18–19*

Power Over *the* Natural World

Water into wine *John 2:1-10*

Miraculous catch of fish *Luke 5:1-11*

Walking on water *Matthew 14:22-33*

Calming the storm *Mark 4:35-41*

Feeding 5000 *John 6:1-14*

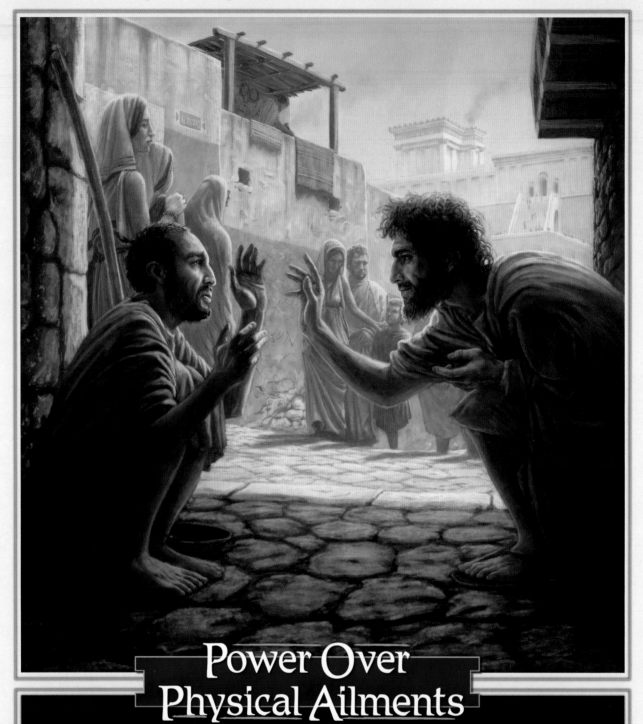

Power Over Physical Ailments

Healing a woman's blood flow *Luke 8:43–48*

Healing the centurion's servant *Luke 7:1–10*

Healing ten lepers *Luke 17:12–19*

Healing the man with dropsy *Luke 14:1–4*

Healing the withered hand *Mark 3:1–5*

Healing the paralytic *Mark 2:1–12*

Healing the lame *John 5:5–9*

Healing the deaf/mute *Mark 7:31–37*

Healing the blind *John 9:1–41*

Power Over Death

Jesus raised at least three people from the dead:

Jairus' daughter *Luke 8:49-56*

Widow's son *Luke 7:11-16*

Lazarus *John 11:1-44*

Four days after His friend Lazarus died, Jesus raised him from the dead. As recorded in John 11–12, this remarkable miracle evoked strong reactions. Many of the Jews who had seen Lazarus alive again believed in Jesus, but others did not. Wanting to hide the evidence of Christ's power, the chief priests plotted to kill the man who had just been raised.

Power Over *the* Supernatural

Jesus cast out demons from each of the following:

The boy who was thrown into fires and water Mark 9:17-27

A man in the synagogue of Capernaum Luke 4:31-37

Two men dwelling among the tombs.
The demons were cast into swine. Matthew 8:28-34

the Triumphal Entry

Not long after raising Lazarus from the dead, Jesus entered Jerusalem riding on a colt, the foal of a donkey, as foretold by the prophet Zechariah. Many people spread their clothes and palm branches on the road, a gesture reminiscent of a king's coronation parade. The people hailed Him as the long-awaited Messiah, praising Him with language from the Psalms. *Mark 11:1-11, John 12:12-19*

Cleansing *the* Temple

The next day, Jesus went into the temple, overturned the tables of the money changers, and drove out the people who had converted it into a marketplace. He scolded them and said that the temple was meant to be a house of prayer but they had turned it into a den of thieves. This infuriated the chief priests and they looked for an opportunity to kill Him. *Matthew 21:12–17, Mark 11:12–19*

the Last Supper

On the night of His arrest, Jesus shared one final meal with His disciples. He washed their feet as an example of how they should serve others. And as a symbol of the new covenant, He gave them bread to eat and wine to drink, representing His body and blood that would be sacrificed on the Cross the next day. *Matthew 26:26–29, John 13:1–20*

After being betrayed by one of His disciples, Jesus was arrested, led through multiple trials, beaten, mocked, and accused of blasphemy by the Jewish leaders. Although the Roman governor, Pilate, found no fault in Him, he condemned Jesus to be flogged and then crucified outside Jerusalem on a hill called Calvary—the Place of a Skull.
John 18—19

It is Finished

Just before He died, Jesus said, "It is finished."
In the original language, this referred to a debt that had
been paid in full. In other words, His sacrificial death
paid the full price of our sin debt. *John 19:30*

Followers of other religions generally believe that they
can earn eternal life by performing good deeds. But if
this were true, then the Son of God did not need to
die on the Cross, and Jesus would have been mistaken
when He said that no one could come to God except
through Him. *John 14:6*

Many professing Christians believe that to be saved
they must add good works to faith in Christ. But this
idea neglects the fact that the once-for-all sacrifice of
Jesus Christ was sufficient to pay for all our sins.

Exhibit: **Christ, Cross, Consummation**

Why Was Jesus Crucified?

The Bible explains that death is the penalty for sin, and that without the shedding of blood, there can be no forgiveness. *Romans 6:23, Hebrews 9:22*

For centuries, God's people shed animal blood to cover their sins, but the blood of these creatures could never take away sins. *Hebrews 10:4*

Only a perfect man could pay for our rebellion.
We are all corrupted by sin, so the Son of God
became a man, lived a sinless life, and died on the Cross
as our substitute—the perfect, once-for-all sacrifice for sin.

To confirm that Jesus had died, a soldier pierced His side with a spear, causing blood and water to come out. His body was given to a wealthy man, Joseph of Arimathea, who placed it in his own tomb, burying Him according to Jewish custom. The next day, at the request of the chief priests and Pharisees, Pilate posted guards outside the tomb.
Matthew 27:57–66

Jesus repeatedly told His disciples that
He would die and rise from the dead three days later.
In fact, His Resurrection was the one sign He said He
would give to "an evil and adulterous generation."
Matthew 12:39–40

After He rose from the dead, Jesus proved that
He was alive again as He appeared
to various people over the next 40 days.
He walked and talked with them, and
He ate and drank with them.

Mary Magdalene *John 20:14–17*

The other women who visited the tomb *Matthew 28:9–10*

Two disciples on the road to Emmaus *Luke 24:13–32*

Simon Peter *Luke 24:34*

The disciples without Thomas *John 20:19–25*

The disciples with Thomas *John 20:26–29*

Seven disciples at Sea of Galilee *John 21:1–14*

Hillside in Galilee *Matthew 28:16–17*

Over 500 people at once *1 Corinthians 15:6*

James *1 Corinthians 15:7*

The disciples at the Mount of Olives *Luke 24:50–51, Acts 1:9*

On the third day, several women set out for the tomb while it was still
dark. There was an earthquake; an angel rolled away the stone and
terrified the guards. He told the women, "Do not be afraid, for I know
that you seek Jesus who was crucified. He is not here; for He is risen,
as He said. Come, see the place where the Lord lay."
Matthew 28:1–6

And Thomas answered and said to Him, "My Lord and my God!"

Jesus said to him, "Thomas, because you have seen Me, you have believed. Blessed are those who have not seen and yet have believed."

John 20:28–29

He is Risen

The Resurrection of Jesus Christ demonstrated much more than just His power over the grave. It also gives us confidence in our hope of eternal life.

This amazing miracle demonstrates that God fully endorsed the work and claims of Jesus. This is particularly significant in regard to Christ's claims of divinity. If Jesus was not God in the flesh, as He claimed, then why would God respond by fulfilling a prediction that confirms the truth of Christ's claims? Therefore, the Resurrection of Jesus Christ proves both His divinity and that He had God's absolute approval.

The Resurrection also grants believers in Christ a preview of the future in that they will also be raised in glorified bodies. Our corruptible and mortal bodies will become incorruptible and immortal. *I Corinthians 15:53*

the Ascension

Forty days after the Resurrection, Christ's followers watched Him ascend into heaven from the Mount of Olives. Two angels appeared and asked them why they were gazing up into heaven, before informing them that Jesus would return from heaven in the same way.

Acts 1:9-10

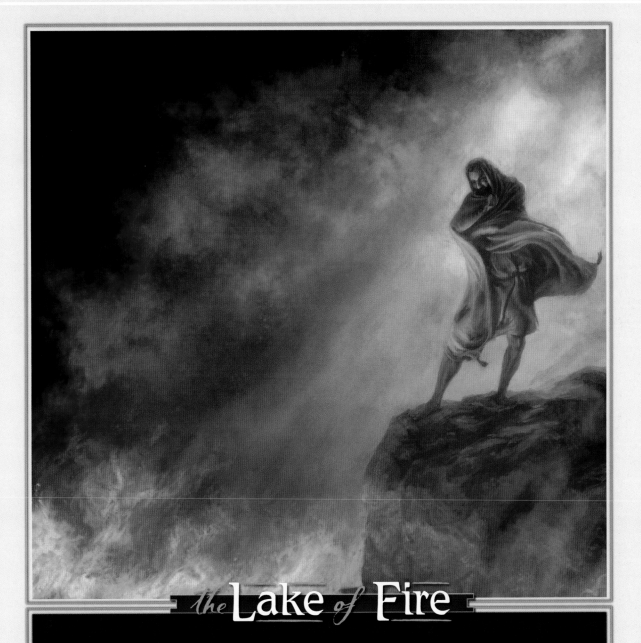

the Lake of Fire

But the cowardly, unbelieving, abominable, murderers, sexually immoral, sorcerers, idolaters, and all liars, their place will be the lake that burns with fire and brimstone. This is the second death.

Revelation 21:8

the New Jerusalem

Then I saw the holy city—the New Jerusalem—coming down out of heaven from God...He will live with them and be their God. And He will wipe away every tear from their eyes; there will no longer be any death, mourning, crying, or pain, for the former things have passed away. *Revelation 21:2-4*

While he was in exile on the Island of Patmos,
the Apostle John received a vision from Jesus Christ
that concluded with a glimpse of the judgment of the
wicked and the future hope of the righteous.

As stated by the angels at His ascension, Jesus Christ will come back to earth.

He will judge the living and the dead in righteousness (Acts 17:31).
While no man knows the timing of the Lord's return, the Bible clearly teaches
that Jesus will physically set foot on earth again.

The Second Coming will not be merely a spiritual event,
as proposed by certain groups.

Where will You spend Eternity?

The eternal destiny of every person is dependent upon his or her relationship
to Jesus Christ. Those who remain in unbelief, rejecting His completed work on
the Cross, sacrificial death, and Resurrection from the dead,
will suffer eternally in the lake of fire.

All who repent of their sins and believe in the Lord Jesus Christ,
trusting in His sacrificial death and Resurrection,
will enjoy everlasting life with their Creator and Savior.

First Adam

The message of the Creation Museum can be summarized by
looking at the first Adam and the Last Adam. God created
a perfect world—no death, no disease, no suffering—and He gave
the first Adam authority over it. When Adam rebelled against
his Creator, he brought God's judgment of death, suffering, and
the Curse upon this world. Like the first Adam, we have all
sinned against God. Consequently, we all deserve the penalty
for our sin—death and condemnation.

Last Adam

Jesus Christ is the Last Adam. He came to redeem what the first Adam
had destroyed. As the first Adam brought death into this world through his sin,
the Last Adam came to live a sinless life, die on the Cross to pay for our sins,
and conquer death by rising from the grave.
One day He will return and put an end to death,
disease, suffering, and the Curse.
All who have received His forgiveness will dwell eternally
with Him in the new heavens and new earth.

Chasmosaurus (KAS-mo-SAWR-us)

Name means: "opening or chasm lizard"
Height: 10 feet (3 m)
Length: 16-20 feet (5-6 m)
Weight: 8,000 pounds (3600 kg)
Described: 1914 by Lawrence M. Lambe
(discovered in 1902)

Family: Ceratopsidae
Where found: Texas, Alberta (Canada)
Layer found in: Upper Cretaceous (~2348 BC)
Diet after the Fall: herbivore (plant eater)

Interesting Facts:

Named for the large openings found in the frill (the large bone section that protrudes from the top of the skull). The difference in frill sizes is strong evidence of sexual dimorphism (differences between male and female). It is one of the best-known horned dinosaurs, with many specimens. Some bone beds contained more than 100 individuals. Skin of *Chasmosaurus* has been found preserved as fossils.

Protoceratops (PRO-to-SER-a-tops)

Name means: "first horned face"
Height: 3 feet (1 m)
Length: 6-10 feet (1.6-3 m)
Weight: 900 pounds (408 kg)
Described: 1923 by Walter Granger
and Walter K. Gregory

Family: Protoceratopsidae
Where found: Mongolia, China
Layer found in: Upper Cretaceous (~2348 BC)
Diet after the Fall: herbivore (plant eater)

Interesting Facts:

Originally named based on the evolutionary belief that this was the first horned dinosaur that gave rise to the other horned dinosaurs. The species *Protoceratops andrewsi* was named for its discoverer, an adventurous fossil hunter named Roy Chapman Andrews whose exploits were the basis for the movie character Indiana Jones.

This is one of the best-known dinosaurs because many specimens in all stages of life have been found. Although they had no horn, many had a thickened area of bone extending from above the snout to between the eyes. Those that had the larger bony bumps on the face also had larger frills, suggesting sexual dimorphism (physical differences between male and female).

Many nests and eggs have been found, containing 12-18 eggs laid in a three-tier spiral. The eggs were elongated and measured about 8 inches (20 cm) long. Many eggs were intact and some contained bone fragments from the tiny embryos. A famous fossil found in Mongolia includes a *Protoceratops* and *Velociraptor* locked in battle, which could be preserved only if something buried the dinosaurs suddenly while in combat.

Ornitholestes (or-NITH-o-LES-teez)

Name means: "bird robber"
Height: 1-3 feet (0.3-1.0 m)
Length: 6-7 feet (1.8-2.1 m)
Weight: 25 pounds (11 kg)
Described: 1903 by Henry Fairfield Osborn

Family: Ornitholestidae
Where found: Wyoming, Utah
Layer found in: Upper Jurassic (~2348 BC)
Diet after the Fall: carnivore (meat eater)

Interesting Facts:

Originally named because its grasping hands were thought to catch birds or raid nests before the dinosaur would quickly flee. It was later discovered that the specimen had the wrong hands.

With an extremely light skeleton made of hollow bones, long legs, and a long tail, this dinosaur was well designed for running. The tail made up more than half the total body length and was perfectly designed to serve as a counterbalance when running. It is known only from a single specimen.

Stegosaurus (STEG-o-SAWR-us)

Name means: "roof or cover lizard"
Height: 8-14 feet (2.4-4.3 m)
Length: 25-30 feet (7.6-9.1 m)
Weight: 4,000-7,000 pounds (1800-3200 kg)
Described: 1877 by Othniel Charles Marsh

Family: Stegosauridae
Where found: Colorado, Utah, Wyoming
Layer found in: Upper Jurassic (~2348 BC)
Diet after the Fall: herbivore (plant eater)

Interesting Facts:

Named for the large plates on its back, which were originally believed to lie flat on the back and protect the dinosaur from predators. Modern scientists now believe the plates were upright and arranged in two rows along the back.

Some plates measure up to 2½ feet (0.8 m) tall. Instead of being solid, they have tube-like passages running throughout them. Many believe that these passages contained a vast array of blood vessels and helped with thermoregulation (regulation of body temperature).

These dinosaurs had an array of large spines on the tail, some measuring 4 feet (1.3 m), most likely used for defense. They had a toothless beak and small cheek teeth. *Stegosaurus* had a small brain, about the size of a walnut, weighing around 2.5-2.9 ounces (70-80 grams). Their hip region had an enlarged spinal cord, which was once considered to be a second brain or nerve center to control the back part of the animal, but more recent studies suggest that they may have been energy storage centers for muscles.

Heterodontosaurus
(HET-e-ro-DON-to-SAWR-us)

Name means: "different-toothed lizard"
Height: 12-20 inches (0.3-0.5 m)
Length: 3-5 feet (1-1.5 m)
Weight: 40-42 pounds (18-19 kg)
Described: 1962 by Alfred W. Compton and Alan J. Charig

Family: Heterodontosauridae
Where found: South Africa
Layer found in: Lower Jurassic (~2348 BC)
Diet after the Fall: herbivore (plant eater)

Interesting Facts:

Unlike many reptiles that have only one type of tooth, *Heterodontosaurus* had three types of teeth. The front teeth were small and likely used for cutting off leaves and stems. The second type was a large pair of tusks that may have served only for sexual displays. The third type of teeth was tall and squared off and well designed for chewing. It may have been a fast runner on two legs, but it also may have been able to walk on all four legs. It had five fingers, and two appear to have been opposable.

Dsungaripterus
(jung-gah-RIP-ter-us or dzung-gah-RIP-ter-us)

Name means: "Junggar Basin wing"
Length: 3.2 feet (1 m)
Wingspan: 10-12 feet (3-3.6 m)
Weight: 22 pounds (10 kg)
Described: 1964 by Chung Chien Young

Family: Dsungaripteridae
Where found: China, Mongolia
Layer found in: Upper Jurassic and Lower Cretaceous (~2348 BC)
Diet after the Fall: carnivore (meat eater)

Interesting Facts:

Named for the location it was first discovered—the Junggar Basin, Xinjiang Province, China. The first specimen was found in a Lower Cretaceous layer of rock in China, and a later specimen was found in Upper Jurassic rocks in Tanzania.

The bones are hollow and lightweight, making flight easier. They had large brains and are believed to have had good eyesight. The wings were covered with a leathery skin that was strong and durable yet lightweight.

Dsungaripterus had an unusual bony crest that ran along the top of the beak to the space between the eyes. The differences in the crest may distinguish males and females, but no one is sure. The head and neck were just over 3 feet (1 m) in length and made up over half of the total body length.

The long jaws curved upward with a pointed tip, sometimes described as "a pair of flying tweezers." There were no teeth in the front of the long jaw, but they did have knobby teeth in back. Some believe the toothless part of the jaws was designed for catching and removing shellfish and worms from cracks in rocks or on the sandy or muddy beaches. The teeth in the back would have been useful for crushing the shells of shellfish.

Archaeopteryx (AHR-kee-OP-ter-iks)

Name means: "ancient wing"
Length: 1-1.5 feet (0.3-0.5 m)
Weight: 11-18 ounces (312-510 g)
Wingspan: 1.5 feet (0.5 m)
Described: 1861 by Hermann von Meyer

Family: Archaeopterygidae
Where found: Solnhofen, Germany
Layer found in: Upper Jurassic (~2348 BC)
Diet after the Fall: carnivore (meat eater)

Interesting Facts:

Named based on the false belief that this creature was an early stage in the evolution of birds. The species was named *lithographica* because it was discovered in the fine-grained limestone slabs used for lithography (a type of printing).

Evolutionists once believed that *Archaeopteryx* was an ancestor of modern birds.

Besides typical bird features (feathers, light bone structure, wishbone, and reduced fingers), *Archaeopteryx* also had teeth, three claws on each wing, abdominal ribs, a long bony tail, and a flat sternum. *Archaeopteryx* was about the size of a crow and appears to have been a good flyer.

Archaeopteryx does not support the current false belief that dinosaurs evolved into birds. Through much research, even most evolutionists now consider *Archaeopteryx* to be a true bird. *Archaeopteryx*: a true perching bird!

Ceratosaurus (se-RAT-o-SAWR-us)

Name means: "horned lizard"
Height: 6-8 feet (2-2.4 m)
Length: 15-20 feet (4.5-6 m)
Weight: 1,000-2,000 pounds (450-900 kg)
Described: 1884 by Othniel Charles Marsh

Family: Ceratosauridae
Where found: Colorado, Utah
Layer found in: Upper Jurassic (~2348 BC)
Diet after the Fall: carnivore (meat eater); probably also a scavenger

Interesting Facts:

The horn on this dinosaur's snout might have served to distinguish male from female, or it could have been used as a defensive or offensive weapon. Some suggest that hatchlings used the horn to help break out of their eggs. *Ceratosaurus* appeared to have had large eyes, indicating excellent eyesight (a trait common among predators and scavengers).

Velociraptor (va-ʟᴏss-ah-RAP-tor)

Name means: "swift robber"
Height: 2-3 feet (0.6-1.0 m)
Length: 5-6 feet (1.5-2.0 m)
Weight: 33-60 pounds (15-27 kg)
Described: 1924 by Henry Fairfield Osborn

Family: Dromaeosauridae
Where found: Mongolia, China
Layer found in: Upper Cretaceous (~2348 BC)
Diet after the Fall: carnivore (meat eater)

Interesting Facts:

Named because it appeared to be a fast-moving dinosaur that robbed the nests of other dinosaurs. *Velociraptor* has a long, stiff tail, large eyes, large hands, and a large 4-inch (10 cm) retractable claw on the second toe of the hind foot. The long, low skull helps distinguish *Velociraptor* from other dromaeosaurid dinosaurs.

Some studies have suggested that *Velociraptor* could run nearly 40 mph (60 kph) for short bursts, making them a dangerous predator. A famous fossil found in Mongolia includes a *Protoceratops* and *Velociraptor* locked in combat. To preserve such an event required sudden burial.

The movie *Jurassic Park* took huge license in how it portrayed *Velociraptors*. To look more ferocious, they appeared nearly three times larger than the fossils and displayed intelligence exceeding some of the people they were hunting.

Tyrannosaurus rex (ti-ʀᴀɴ-ᴏ-SAWR-us)

Name means: "tyrant lizard king"
Height: 15-17 feet (4.5-5.0 m)
Length: 40-43 feet (12-13 m)
Weight: 12,000-15,000 pounds (5400-6800 kg)
Described: 1905 by Henry Fairfield Osborn
Family: Tyrannosauridae

Where found: Colorado, Montana, New Mexico, N. Dakota, S. Dakota, Texas, Utah, Wyoming, Alberta and Saskatchewan (Canada)
Layer found in: Upper Cretaceous (~2348 BC)
Diet after the Fall: carnivore (meat eater); probably also a scavenger

Interesting Facts:

Probably the most well-known dinosaur of all, it has been portrayed in movies for over sixty years, including the *Jurassic Park* movie series.

Tyrannosaurus rex had teeth up to 12 inches (0.3 m) long and a skull up to 5 feet (1.5 m) long. The position of the eye sockets and narrowing of the snout indicate that it may have had binocular vision. Most believe that *T. rex* was an active predator, but more recent studies indicate that it may have been too slow to hunt and mostly scavenged for food.

Fossilized skin of *T. rex* has been found, indicating rapid preservation. In 1997, a scientist discovered red blood cells in the femur of a *T. rex*. In 2005, soft tissue was found in another bone. These findings are consistent with the hypothesis that dinosaur fossils are not millions of years old and that they were buried suddenly and recently.

Thescelosaurus
(thes-kel-o-SAWR-us)

Name means: "surprising lizard"
Height: 4 feet (1.2 m)
Length: 10-13 feet (3-3.6 m)
Weight: 660 pounds (300 kg)
Described: 1913 by Charles W. Gilmore

Family: Hypsilophodontidae
Where found: Colorado, South Dakota, Wyoming, Alberta and Saskatchewan (Canada)
Layer found in: Upper Cretaceous (~2348 BC)
Diet after the Fall: herbivore (plant eater)

Interesting Facts:

Named because the discoverers were surprised when they found that it represented a new form of orthopodous dinosaur.

In 1993, a fossil was discovered near Buffalo, South Dakota, that revealed the first fossilized dinosaur heart. A CT-scan showed that it had four chambers, indicating that the dinosaur was warm-blooded, although some reptiles still living today, such as crocodiles and alligators, have four-chambered hearts and are cold-blooded. Whether dinosaurs were warm-blooded or cold-blooded is still a subject of study and debate. The preservation of delicate internal tissue of a heart indicates burial under sudden and catastrophic conditions, such as the global Flood of Noah's day.

Struthiomimus
(STROOTH-ee-o-MIME-us)

Name means: "ostrich mimic"
Height: 6-8 feet (1.8-2.5 m)
Length: 10-14 feet (3-4 m)
Weight: 330-440 pounds (154-200 kg)
Described: 1916 by Henry Fairfield Osborn
Family: Ornithomimidae

Where found: Alberta (Canada)
Layer found in: Upper Cretaceous (~2348 BC)
Diet after the Fall: omnivore (meat and plant eater)

Interesting Facts:

Named because its body shape resembled an ostrich. It appears to have been a fast runner that could run away from most predators. *Struthiomimus* had no teeth but a sharp beak, leading to much speculation about its diet. Perhaps it tore meat with its sharp beak. Its long, powerful forearm may have been used for grasping eggs, small animals, insects, or even branches to help forage on leaves and buds.

Rhamphorhynchus
(ʀᴀᴍ-fo-RING-kus)

Name means: "beak snout"
Length: 1-2 feet (0.3-.06 m)
Wingspan: 3-6 feet (0.9-1.8 m)
Weight: 4 pounds (1.8 kg)
Described: 1847 by Hermann von Meyer

Family: Rhamphorynchidae
Where found: England, Germany, Tanzania
Layer found in: Upper Jurassic (~2348 BC)
Diet after the Fall: piscivore (fish eater)

Interesting Facts:

Named for the beak-like projection on the snout. This flying reptile apparently caught fish by skimming the lower jaw in the water as it flew above the surface, much like skimmers do today, snapping its jaw shut and holding the fish with its sharp teeth.

Some well-preserved specimens had throat pouches, much like pelicans, and could have stored fish in the pouch until it landed. It had a long tail with a diamond-shaped flap of skin at the tip, which may have been used as a rudder in flight.

Rhamphorhynchus was a pterosaur, not a dinosaur. A number of specimens have been found and classified in this genus, but in 1995 many of the different species were reinterpreted as variations of the same species, reflecting different stages of growth and differences between males and females.

Triceratops (try-SER-a-tops)

Name means: "three-horned face"
Height: 10 feet (3 m)
Length: 25-30 feet (7.6-9.1 m)
Weight: 8,800-24,000 pounds (4000-10,900 kg)
Described: 1889 by Othniel Charles Marsh
Family: Ceratopsidae

Where found: Colorado, Montana, N. Dakota, S. Dakota, Wyoming, Alberta and Saskatchewan (Canada)
Layer found in: Upper Cretaceous (~2348 BC)
Diet after the Fall: herbivore (plant eater)

Interesting Facts:

Named for the three horns on the skull. The first fossil found of *Triceratops* was a pair of horn cores that were misidentified as a species of bison. Many believe that the horns and solid head frill helped with defense against predators. Some skulls are huge, up to 10 feet (3 m) long, and they have horns up to 4 foot (1.3 m) long.

Triceratops had a strong beak, which apparently tore off plant material, and it had strong teeth for chewing.

Over the years, twenty species of *Triceratops* have been named, but today it is believed that there are only two species and that many of the differences reflect various ages of life and differences between males and females.

Edaphosaurus
(ah-DAFF-oh-SAWR-us)

Name means: "ground or pavement lizard"
Height: 3-5 feet (0.8-1.4 m)
Length: 10-11 feet (3 m)
Weight: 660 pounds (300 kg)
Described: 1882 by Edward Drinker Cope
Family: Edaphosauridae

Where found: Texas, Czech Republic
Layer found in: Upper Carboniferous and
                    Lower Permian (~2348 BC)
Diet after the Fall: herbivore (plant eater)

Interesting Facts:

Named for its flat teeth. The distinguishing feature, however, is the large sail on its back. The bones in the sail were thicker and more knobby than those found in a similar animal called *Dimetrodon*. The large sails may have been used for sexual display or for regulating body temperature.

Edaphosaurus was not a dinosaur but is classified as a pelycosaur. Note how the legs sprawl out from the sides of the body and do not stand upright directly below the body, as is characteristic of dinosaurs.

Statement refers to sculpture shown in exhibit but not in this book

BUGS OR INSECTS?

Did you know that not all insects are bugs, but all bugs are insects?

And spiders are not bugs or insects at all; they are arachnids.

Insects make up the largest group of animals in the world. Within this enormous group is a smaller group called true bugs. So, how are true bugs different from other insects, and where do spiders fit in?

Classification of creepy crawlies can get confusing, so we've broken down some of the big groups to show you where they fit in.

← [True bugs are displayed in the case to the **LEFT.**]

[Male/female pairs of many insect groups are displayed in the case to the **RIGHT.** Throughout the insectorium, when pairs are shown, the male is to the left of the female.] →

INSECTS VS. ARACHNIDS

[Insects]

6 Legs

3 Body Parts

Wings (Often)

Some insects are true bugs, which have piercing-sucking mouth parts and if winged, partially or totally membranous (thin, often transparent) forewings, with hindwings that are membranous.

[Arachnids]

8 Legs

2 Body Parts

No Wings

Arachnids are creatures like spiders, scorpions, ticks, etc.

AMAZING DESIGN

God loves variety! Nowhere can we see this more clearly than among the insects.

From the beautiful to the bizarre, insects challenge the idea of evolution. The incredible details of color and design stand as spectacular witnesses to our loving and imaginative Creator.

There are over one million identified insect species today, with probably many more to be discovered.

God created animals and plants with the ability to adapt to new and changing environments by equipping them with tremendous genetic versatility. This diversity prepared them for the "struggle for survival" that followed man's sin and the dramatic changes in ecosystems that resulted from Noah's Flood.

> There are over **ONE MILLION** identified insect species today, with probably many more to be discovered.

Beetles are the single largest group of living things on earth in terms of number of species and total population.

Beetles are just one type of insect. They can easily be distinguished from other types of insects by the straight line down their backs dividing the two forewings, or elytra. These wings are not used for flying but are tough coverings that protect the hind wings used for flight.

The thin, transparent wings underneath the elytra have numerous creases and hinges that allow the beetle to fold them up like a Navy jet fighter parked on an aircraft carrier. This brilliant design allows beetles to drill into trees, plow underground, swim underwater, or squeeze into tight places. But when they need to cover ground in a hurry, nearly all beetles can unfurl their hind wings and fly.

> The two cases to the **RIGHT** show many types of beetles. →

METALLIC BEETLES

For thousands of years, artists have used many of the patterns found on insects in their artwork, and many have even used vivid and jewel-like beetles as decorative jewelry.

The beautiful colors are a combination of pigments and structural design that only reflect certain light. For example, the metallic appearance of the gold and silver jewel beetles is perfectly constructed to refract only those colors. Scientists are studying this incredible structure and the use of polarized light, but they still do not fully comprehend it. Clearly an all-wise and wonderful Creator designed this beauty!

THINK CRITICALLY:

How could intricate design features such as structural refraction and use of polarized light have slowly evolved?

While explaining why His followers shouldn't worry, Jesus talked about God's care for His creation and stated the following:

"So why do you worry about clothing? Consider the lilies of the field, how they grow: they neither toil nor spin; and yet I say to you that even Solomon in all his glory was not arrayed like one of these. Now if God so clothes the grass of the field, which today is, and tomorrow is thrown into the oven, will He not much more clothe you, O you of little faith?" (Matthew 6:28–30)

Looking at these beautiful little creatures that God has made should make you realize just how much He cares for you.

LIFE OF A DUNG BEETLE

It's a dirty job, but somebody's got to do it. Dung beetles spend their lives eating, moving, and breeding in dung. We may cringe at their way of life, but if these humble recyclers had not been created, we would live in a smellier, fly-infested world.

Some members of this spectacular worldwide cleaning crew roll dung balls to their egg-laying sites. Others tunnel under the manure and bury it for their larvae to eat, and others breed and live directly in the muck. They all work hard, fast, and without complaint because they are doing what they were made to do.

BATTLING BEETLES

Male stag beetles are famous for their battles.

They frequently joust for the right to mate with a nearby female. The victor lifts the vanquished, thus breaking the loser's foothold on the branch where they meet. The falling beetle survives and flies or crawls away to seek less-contested territory.

Both male and female stag beetles also fight for food or territory. These cases include only male stag beetles because the females show much less variation.

[Stag beetles are named for the antler-like jaws of the larger males.]

DOES THE BEETLE GET BIGGER?

People often see a small beetle and think that it's a "baby" beetle that will grow larger, but in reality, after the adult beetle emerges from its pupal cell, it does not grow anymore. All the growth takes place during the larval stage.

FLOWER BEETLES

Here are some of the largest and most colorful beetles around.

Similar to their fancy fluttering friends the butterflies, these beetles like to visit flowers, fruits, and flowing sap from trees.

Appropriately named "flower beetles" or "fruit chafers," they are also very important as pollinators, and their larvae help decompose fallen logs and other plant matter.

Their amazing array of colors and patterns, given by God, make them a favorite group of insects to collect and study.

GOLIATH BEETLES:

Have you ever tied a string to a june bug and let it fly? African children do the same thing with the Goliath beetle—their version of our june bug—that reaches enormous proportions. They love to watch these huge beetles fly like little remote-controlled helicopters.

Considered one of the world's heaviest insects and named after the famous giant in the Bible, Goliath, these living tanks are attracted to the oozing sap of trees or ripe fruit. They cannot bite, but beware of placing a finger between their prothorax and mesothorax because these can snap shut in an instant. Ouch!

[THINK CRITICALLY]

How could something so bulky and heavy even fly? Chance mutations through slow evolution **OR** purposeful design?

BEETLE LIFE CYCLE

1 → After mating, the female lays eggs in the soil. The eggs will hatch about 30 days later.

2 → Only about 8 mm long (less than ½ inch), a tiny larva emerges from each egg.

3 → The larva must go through three stages of growth called instars. It will molt (shed its skin) between each stage. Rhinoceros beetle larvae curl into a C-shape when at rest.

4 → The insect spends as much as two years as a larva, during which time it just eats and eats and eats. Ironically, while it's in this stage of continuous eating, the larva may become a meal for something else. Rhinoceros beetle larvae convert dirt and other matter to high-protein food.

5 → In its third larval stage, called L3, the *Megasoma actaeon* is thought to be the heaviest insect in the world, with some weighing in at 200 grams—that's nearly half a pound!

6 → The larva digs a pupal cell, a chamber in the dirt where it will go through its next stage of metamorphosis. Amazingly, the larva creates a chamber appropriately sized for its adult form, horns and all. The pupal stage lasts about 38 days.

7 → An incredible transformation takes place in the pupal cell. The insect takes on a whole new body form with completely new structures. The adult does not resemble the larva in appearance or behavior. It digs its way out of the dirt, flies off, and then looks for a mate.

Do Insects Have
NOSES?

BEETLE KINDS

Check out these massive insects!

These are rhinoceros beetles, so called because of the horns. Rhinoceros beetles comprise a huge group of many species, large and small. The specimens displayed here are very large examples of some of the biggest beetle species in the world.

While these represent different groups, or genera, of rhinoceros beetles, they show many similarities. In fact, some of them can breed with each other, even though they are different species.

The classification of species is a man-made category and is not the same as the "kind" mentioned repeatedly in Genesis. Species that can crossbreed probably belong to the same created kind.

The similarities among the many varieties of rhinoceros beetles, as well as the ability of many to crossbreed, suggest that all rhinoceros beetles belong to the same created kind. The Creator gave their ancestors the genetic potential to produce many wonderful variations.

"Then God said, Let the earth bring forth the living creature according to its kind: cattle and creeping thing and beast of the earth, each according to its kind; and it was so."

– Genesis 1:24

GIANT DRAGONFLY

"We're going to need the BIG fly swatter!"

The fossil record contains supersize versions of a number of creatures, including insects such as Meganeura, the giant dragonfly (also called a "griffinfly").

Modern dragonflies are displayed in the case below. Since no seagull-sized dragonflies fly the skies today, people wonder how they grew so large and why they all died out. Many evolutionists and some early creationists believe that giant growth was once fueled by "hyperoxia" (excessive oxygen) in the atmosphere's past.

God provided the earth with sufficient oxygen early in the Creation Week. Also, plants would have been producing it on Day Three and animals would have needed it to breathe by Day Five. We cannot be sure if the atmosphere before Noah's Flood was much different from today.

Some researchers have suggested that higher atmospheric oxygen caused longer lifespans and gigantism in the world before the Flood. But in recent times, researchers found that excessive oxygen was usually a detriment (this is why antioxidants are good). However, genetics, physiology, and changes in climate (e.g., the Ice Age after the Flood) may better explain these declines in life expectancy and size since the Flood.

Normal variation of some created kinds of insects may have simply included gigantic varieties. Perhaps the climate changes in the post-Flood world were too stressful for many animal varieties that tended to grow large before they laid eggs. With more extreme winters (coming sooner) and shorter growing seasons, insects would have less time to mature and reproduce, giving smaller types an advantage—while their larger counterparts would have been eliminated through the process some call "natural selection."

The actual cause for the disappearance of these giant insects may be a combination of these ideas or it may be something we have not yet considered.

[
Genetics, physiology, and changes in climate (e.g., the Ice Age after the Flood) may explain the declines in life expectancy and size of dragonflies since the Flood.
]

INSECT FOSSILS

The fossil record confirms the biblical account of Noah's Flood. God created insects and other life forms during the Creation Week thousands of years ago, and billions of creatures died in the global Flood of Noah's day.

PRESERVATION SHOWS RAPID BURIAL

What happens when an insect, or any animal, dies? It does not usually become a fossil. Something has to stop the normal scavenging and decay processes in order for the animal to be preserved.

The global Flood, as recorded in Genesis, explains most of the plethora of fossils found around the world. Everything that had the breath of life in its nostrils, other than those saved on Noah's Ark, died in the year-long catastrophe. Mud, sandstone, and volcanic ash buried the carcasses of billions of dead things, protecting the remains from scavengers and preventing full decay.

DID NOAH TAKE INSECTS ON THE ARK?

Obviously many insects survived the Flood, but you may wonder how. The Bible does not specifically say whether Noah was to take insects on board the Ark, but God did command him to take two of every kind of creeping thing and flying thing. Since insects do not have the "breath of life" in their nostrils (they don't have nostrils), they may not have been included.

If Noah did not specifically load insects on the Ark to save them, many certainly went aboard in the wood, supplies, food, and on the other animals. Others could have survived on huge mats of floating vegetation and decaying organic material. During cold or stormy weather, many insects are able to go through a diapause stage (similar to hibernation) or a long pupa stage between larva and adult, and this ability could have allowed many kinds of insects to survive.

GOD'S INSECT CHOIR

Grasshoppers, katydids, and crickets are some of the most musical insects.

Many males "sing" during the cover of night by rubbing a rough edge of a body part across some combination of other body parts, such as the legs, wings, or abdomen.

This music is critical to their life cycle because they sing to attract females. A female will hear the music and respond by tracking the sound to locate a male. This matchmaking technique requires precise, specialized equipment and responsive behavior. The male must be able to make the proper sound; the female must hear and recognize the music of her own species; and she must be able to locate the male by sound.

Think Critically!

How could males evolve the equipment and behavior skills to sing at the same time as the females evolved ears and the instinct to locate the males by their songs? The mating calls of grasshoppers clearly bear the fingerprint of the Great Designer.

BREAKFAST OF PROPHETS:

In Leviticus 11:22, God gave the Hebrews grasshoppers, crickets, katydids, and locusts as food. John the Baptist actually lived on locusts and wild honey in the wilderness (Matthew 3:4).

DESIGNED TO HIDE

These cases display some of the world's most amazing examples of mimicry: the phasmatodeans and mantids.

Cryptic colorations, more commonly known as camouflage, allow these creatures to blend into their surroundings like "phantoms," hence their order name: Phasmatodea. Notice the walking stick and walking leaf and how closely they resemble their habitat.

Their heads look like emerging buds, and they can even move their bodies in a slow, rocking motion that looks like a branch or leaf swaying in a gentle breeze.

[THINK CRITICALLY!]

How could these creatures slowly develop by chance over time from "simpler" ancestral forms without already having the information required for these elaborate disguises?

Walking Leaves

The name "walking leaves" (Family: Phyllidae) wonderfully describes these living examples of God's creativity. Closely observe the intricate patterns that perfectly mimic the veins of a leaf, even with spots of discoloration that real leaves often have.

Their colors vary from vivid greens and bright yellows, to mottled shades of brown. Rarer are the oranges and reds, completing the full spectrum of leaf coloration.

Some species even have bite-mark patterns on the edge of their bodies. The disguise is so convincing that even their own species have been observed taking a nibble from each other!

Why be
BEAUTIFUL?

Drab-colored insects survive and reproduce successfully, so why would these fantastic colors and artistic patterns have evolved, if evolution were true?

Many people think that looking good helps insects attract mates. However, males locate females using the sense of smell, not sight.

In a few cases, bright coloration in insects seems to warn potential predators, but for the vast majority, their beauty provides no apparent survival or reproductive advantage.

From the Christian's viewpoint, the indescribable beauty throughout nature does serve a purpose—to proclaim the glory of the Creator.

The ultimate Engineer-Designer-Artist-Architect-Genius left His fingerprints throughout creation so that we can see what we most need to see—we are not alone and we have a purpose.

THE NEXT TIME YOU SEE AN INSECT DOING WHAT IT WAS DESIGNED TO DO

SUCH AS A BUTTERFLY BOUNCING IN THE BREEZE, OR AN ANT PERFORMING HER ENDLESS TASKS, OR PERHAPS A DRAGONFLY DARTING ABOUT IN THE EVENING TWILIGHT

REMEMBER YOUR CREATOR, AND HOW MUCH MORE HE CARES FOR YOU!

"YOU ARE WORTHY, O LORD, TO RECEIVE GLORY AND HONOR AND POWER; FOR YOU CREATED ALL THINGS, AND BY YOUR WILL THEY EXIST AND WERE CREATED"

– REVELATION 4:11

FEARFULLY &
WONDERFULLY
Made

THE IMAGE OF GOD

All human beings are made in the image of God. Theologians strive to adequately describe all that this truth entails, but we can be confident of the following implications of being made in God's image because they are revealed in His Word.

DISTINCT FROM ANIMALS

After He made the animals, the Lord created the first man and woman, setting them apart by making them in His image and giving them dominion over the animals.

> God said, "Let Us make man in Our image, according to Our likeness. Let them have dominion over the fish of the sea, over the birds of the air, and over the cattle, over all the earth and over every creeping thing that creeps on the earth." (Genesis 1:26)

EVERY PERSON

Though marred by Adam's sin, every human being, both male and female, from the moment of fertilization, is made in God's image, regardless of one's level of development, physical or mental ability, ethnicity, or age.

> So God created man in His own image; in the image of God He created him; male and female He created them. (Genesis 1:27)

IMMEASURABLE VALUE

All human life is precious because we are made in God's image. This fact explains why it is wrong to curse others (James 3:8-9), and why God prescribed a severe penalty for murder.

> "Whoever sheds man's blood, by man his blood shall be shed; for God made man in His own image." (Genesis 9:6)

BIBLICAL VIEW OF THE UNBORN

God's Word teaches that the unborn child is a unique personand fully human. They are also depicted as being just as valuable as those who have already been born.

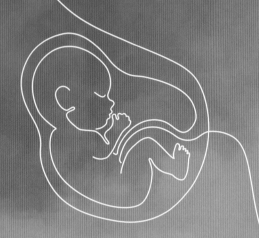

LEAPING FOR JOY

While pregnant with Jesus, Mary visited her relative Elizabeth, who was pregnant with John the Baptist. Elizabeth explained that something special happened when Mary greeted her.

> *"And who am I that the mother of my Lord should come to me? For behold, when the sound of your greeting reached my ears, the baby in my womb leaped for joy."*
> *(Luke 1:43-44)*

The Greek word *brephos* is used here for the baby in the womb and elsewhere for babies already born (Luke 2:12, 18:15, and Acts 7:19).

EQUAL VALUE

In the Mosaic Law, the law of retribution is prescribed for a person who injures or kills an unborn child, showing that the unborn child is viewed with the same dignity and value as one who has been born.

> *If men fight, and hurt a woman with child, so that she gives birth prematurely, yet no harm follows, he shall surely be punished accordingly as the woman's husband imposes on him...and the judges determine. But if any harm follows, then you shall give life for life, eye for eye...*
> *(Exodus 21:22-25)*

Some Bibles mistranslate this passage to speak of a woman who *miscarries* after being struck. This error changes the meaning so that the man is merely fined if the baby dies, and only in danger of "life for life" if the woman perishes.

GOD WITH US (IN THE WOMB)

When the Son of God came to earth in human flesh, He did not come as a grown man. Instead, after being miraculously conceived in Mary, He grew and developed in the womb for roughly nine months before being born.

> *"Behold, the virgin shall be with child and shall bear a Son, and they shall call His name Immanuel," which is translated, "God with us."*
> *(Matthew 1:23)*

God did not send His Son to earth on the night we celebrate as the first Christmas. Instead, the Son arrived on earth approximately nine months earlier when Mary's egg was fertilized.

WE ARE ALL UNIQUE CREATIONS

Every human being has been uniquely created by God. At the very moment the sperm fertilizes the egg, an individual human possessing his or her own combination of DNA, half from the father and half from the mother, begins developing inside the mother.[1]

Far from being merely a clump of cells, a blob of tissue, or a parasite inside the mother, the tiny person in the womb displays incredible complexity and purposeful design. The process of human development from fertilized egg to birth is **a matchless wonder** revealing the Creator's awe-inspiring creativity and care.

[1]Identical twins initially share identical DNA, but minor genetic variations arise due to factors related to DNA replication during their lifetimes.

"BE FRUITFUL AND MULTIPLY"

The Lord spoke these words to Adam and Eve as He blessed them, and He repeated this blessing to Noah's family after the Flood. Until the past century, no one realized the staggering complexity exhibited in the process of sexual reproduction.

Under normal circumstances, each cell in the human body is diploid, meaning that it contains 23 pairs of chromosomes within its nucleus. The sperm and egg are exceptions to this rule. Thanks to a special type of cell division known as meiosis, these haploid sex cells contain just 23 chromosomes.

EGG CELLS

Also known as the ovum, an egg cell is huge compared to other cells, being roughly the size of a grain of salt. The egg develops in a woman's ovaries, and approximately once a month, a single egg with the mother's genetic material is released from an ovary. The egg travels into a fallopian tube where it awaits fertilization.

SPERM CELLS

Approximately 300 million sperm develop in an adult male every day. The head of the sperm is packed with the father's genetic material and the tail is used for propulsion. Upon entering the female reproductive system, the sperm can survive up to five days. Sperm that enter the fallopian tube will have an opportunity to fertilize the egg.

THE JOURNEY OF LIFE BEFORE BIRTH

THE BABY'S AGE

The dates on this timeline show the **embryonic age** of the baby, which begins at the moment of fertilization. Pregnancy dates are usually based on the **gestational age**, which starts from the day of the mother's last menstruation. This common practice yields an age approximately two weeks older than the baby's actual age.

PRIOR TO FERTILIZATION

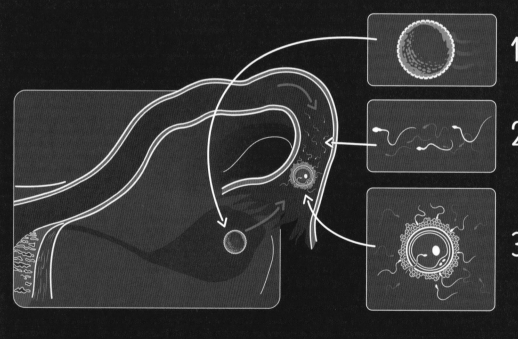

1 Approximately once a month, an egg is released from an ovary and enters the fallopian tube.

2 As sperm travel toward the egg, they react with chemicals in the uterus and fallopian tube, giving sperm greater mobility and an ability to push through the egg's outer layer.

3 Of the millions of sperm cells, only about 10–20 might reach the egg. The first sperm to pass through the egg's outer protective layer and touch the cell membrane will be the one to fertilize the egg.

FERTILIZATION

Fertilization occurs when the father's DNA from the sperm combines with the mother's DNA within the egg. This single cell is referred to as a zygote and is a unique human being made in the image of God.

DAY 2

The cell divides into two cells and is now referred to as an embryo. The embryo continues moving along the fallopian tube to the uterus.

DAY 3

Cell division continues, and when 16 cells are present the little ball is called a morula.

DAY 5

The cells form into a blastula, a spherical layer of cells around a liquid-filled cavity. The outer cells will help form the placenta while an inner cell mass will form the baby's body.

DAY 6

Around the sixth day, the blastula leaves the fallopian tube and begins to implant in the wall of the uterus. During implantation and placental formation, the baby is nourished by uterine glands whose secretion is maintained by hormones from the mother's ovary.

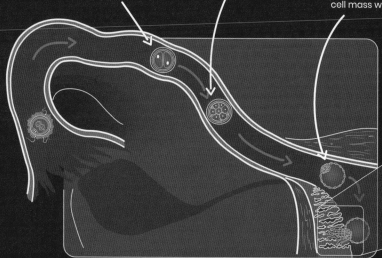

DAY 14

The embryo is now implanted firmly in the uterine wall and will begin to grow rapidly.

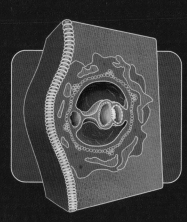

DAY 22

The brain and nervous system have been forming for several days, and the heart begins to beat.

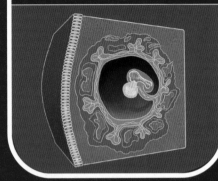

DAY 24

The heart continues to grow, causing a bulge in the baby's midsection, and the structures that make up the eyes and ears have started to form.

DAY 28

The pharyngeal arches are readily apparent. These folds near the embryo's head develop into some of the muscles, bones, and glands in the head and neck area.

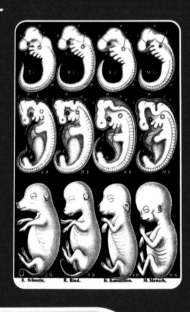

DEADLY DRAWINGS

In 1874, Ernst Haeckel published **fraudulent drawings** of various embryos and referred to these arches as "gill slits" while promoting his thoroughly debunked evolutionary idea known as embryonic recapitulation (i.e., embryonic development echoes alleged evolutionary ancestry). This "gill slit" lie has been used to promote belief in evolution and justify abortion. Despite scientific advancements that have conclusively shown that **humans never go through some sort of fish stage** or any other non-human stage in the womb, Haeckel's fraudulent work continued to appear in museums, textbooks, and scientific literature for over 100 years.

Illustrations in Haeckel's *Anthropogenie* (1874) promoted the myth that embryonic development follows evolutionary ancestry.

MODEL SHOWN ABOVE

DAY 40

The eyes and ears continue forming, and the hands, arms, feet, and legs are easily discerned.

WEEK 8

External genitalia start developing and within a week the baby will be recognizable as a little boy or a little girl. The umbilical cord is easy to see.

WEEK 9

Now that the basic structures of the central nervous system, brain, and other vital organs have been established, the baby takes on a new title: fetus.

WEEK 10

She now spans about 2.5 inches from crown to rump and weighs less than an ounce. Her fingernails are growing in, and her face looks much more like that of a baby who has already been born.

WEEK 11

The baby's fingers begin moving independently and fingerprints have appeared. In baby girls, her tiny ovaries already contain all the eggs she will ever produce—over two million of them.

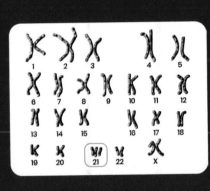

Individuals with three copies of chromosome 21 are said to have Down syndrome, which is also known as Trisomy 21.

PRENATAL GENOCIDE

Prenatal screening and diagnostic tests are frequently performed to identify potential genetic disorders in developing babies. These **flawed tests** are then used to justify terminating those who might have a disorder. For example, in recent years, nearly every baby with **Down syndrome** in Iceland has been aborted. Meanwhile, 98% of babies suspected of having Down syndrome have been aborted in Denmark. England (90%), France (77%), and the United States (67%) are also participating in this prenatal genocide against these precious individuals.[1]

[1] George F. Will, "The Real Down Syndrome Problem: Accepting Genocide," *The Washington Post*, March 14, 2018.

WEEK 12

The placenta has developed all the necessary structures to supply the baby's nourishment. She uses her facial muscles and may even start sucking her thumb.

WEEK 13

Her eyelids are fused, but because she can sense light, the baby will turn away from bright light.

WEEK 14

Fine, soft, unpigmented hair, called lanugo, grows from hair follicles. Since no more hair follicles are produced after birth, those present at birth form all the hairs she will have in her lifetime.

WEEK 15

The baby's hairline grows on her head. She can now move her joints and the soft cartilage of her skeleton begins to be replaced by bone.

WEEK 17

The baby's senses are developing, and she may be able to hear sounds beyond the womb.

WEEK 18

The baby tastes and swallows some of the amniotic fluid around her, and the digestive system begins functioning.

WEEK 19

The baby's fragile skin is coated in a white layer of shed skin cells and oil called vernix, protecting her from the amniotic fluid. Now halfway through her time inside of mom, the baby announces her presence with soft kicks and stretches against her mother's womb.

WEEK 21

Her skin is still translucent, and she is rather thin, but big changes are just around the corner.

Lyla with parents' rings around her arm.

Lyla at 4 years old.

Photos courtesy of Courtney Stensrud
www.hopefaithandrockstars.com

MICRO PREEMIES

Babies born prior to full term are called preemies, due to their premature delivery. Those born prior to 24 weeks (*26 weeks gestational age*) are known as micro preemies. Thanks to medical advancements, micro preemies now enjoy **much higher survival rates**. They may spend months in a NICU, but the number facing lifelong problems from early delivery is decreasing.[2] The youngest micro preemies to survive were born around 20 weeks (*22 weeks gestational age*) and **weighed less than a pound**. For example, Lyla (*pictured here*), was under 20 weeks at birth (*21 weeks, 4 days gestational age*).

[2] https://www.verywellfamily.com/what-is-a-micro-preemie-2748625

WEEK 23

Baby fat begins filling out her skin, and colored hair grows on her head.

WEEK 25

The baby's brain is very active, and she now has a relatively consistent sleep schedule.

WEEK 26

The baby blinks as her eyesight continues to improve, and her eyelashes have grown in.

WEEK 24

The baby "breathes" amniotic fluid as the lungs practice for her first breath of air.

WEEK 30

With each of her systems in place, the baby begins to grow rapidly, gaining about half a pound every week until birth.

WEEK 33

The baby's pupils dilate or contract in response to light, and her kidneys are fully developed.

PLACENTA: SUPER ORGAN

In the womb, the placenta functions as the baby's lungs, liver, kidneys, digestive system, and immune system. Although both the mother's and baby's blood flow through the placenta, they do not mix. If the placenta did not **protect the baby** in this way, the mother's body would fight against the baby's blood with antibodies. At birth, this **selfless servant** becomes unnecessary and is discarded.

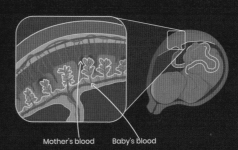

Mother's blood   Baby's blood

WEEK 34

The lanugo hair that covered the baby's body is almost gone, although the layer of vernix that coated her body usually remains until shortly after birth. It is believed that the vernix lubricates the birth process and minimizes evaporative water loss, keeping the baby warm for the first few hours after birth.

WEEKS 37–41

The baby is ready to be born. In preparation for her big move she has been upside down for much of the second half of the pregnancy.

WEEK 36

The lungs and brain fully mature in the final weeks before birth. Also, her eye color is filling in, although if she is born with blue eyes, they might change to a darker color during her first year.

THE JOURNEY OF LIFE BEYOND BIRTH

As shown in these twelve models, the human body undergoes remarkable changes from fertilization until birth. But these modifications are just the beginning. As a person grows, the body continues to change, particularly at puberty, as girls mature into women and boys into men. As people grow older, their bodies break down and they eventually die, consequences of Adam's sin. But death is not the end of human life because all people were created to live forever. For those who believe in Jesus Christ, their bodies will be transformed, and they will dwell eternally with their Creator in a place where there is no more sorrow, pain, tears, or death (Revelation 21:3–4).

MOTHERLY MODIFICATIONS

During the birthing process, the mother's body undergoes specially designed changes to keep her and the baby safe.

Three joints in the mother's pelvis loosen, causing the opening to expand so that the baby can pass through.

When the placenta detaches from the mother's uterus it leaves a gaping wound that would cause her to quickly bleed to death if not for special circular muscles that quickly close each of the affected vessels.

BABY'S FIRST BREATH

Prior to birth, the placenta essentially functions as the baby's lungs, liver, GI tract, kidneys, and more. But in the first few moments after birth, many significant changes occur.

During development, blood bypassed the lungs, taking a shortcut through the heart where it must flow in order to be pumped to the rest of the body. At birth, that shortcut closes so that blood flows to the lungs, and the bypass between the heart's right and left atria closes.

The baby spent her first nine months in fluid, so the blood and lymph systems remove fluid from the lungs and replace it with oxygen, allowing her to take her first breath.

WHEN DOES HUMAN LIFE BEGIN?

This question lies at the heart of some highly contentious issues in our world. From a medical standpoint, there is only one logical answer: **life begins at fertilization**, when the chromosomes from the sperm and the egg combine, forming a genetically unique individual.

This was traditionally called the moment of conception, but in the past few decades conception has often been redefined to refer to the processes from fertilization through implantation of the embryo in the womb.

Our medical knowledge of this process has caused the debate to shift from "When does life begin?" to "When does personhood begin?" or "When do the unborn feel pain?" But these questions avoid the real issue. Whether one refers to the unborn as an embryo, fetus, or baby, we learn from God's Word that a human being made in the image of God is growing and developing within the mother from the moment of fertilization.

THE TRUTH

COUNTERING POPULAR ARGUMENTS FOR ABORTION

A detailed answer to every argument for abortion is beyond the scope of this exhibit, but brief responses are given to some of them to provide a proper perspective and illustrate how most of them distract from the real issue: the baby in the womb is a human being made in God's image (Genesis 1:26), and the Lord hates the shedding of innocent blood (Proverbs 6:16-17).

"The embryo or fetus is just a clump of cells."
As this exhibit has demonstrated, ultrasounds and other medical advancements have shown this to be an outdated argument.

"It's a woman's body, so it should be her choice."
The baby does develop inside of the mother whose body undergoes significant changes, but the baby is not part of the mother's body. A pregnant woman's body does not have four arms, four legs, and two heads. Abortion destroys the baby's body—not the mother's body.

"What if a woman became pregnant through rape or incest?"
In these tragic situations, the baby should not be killed for someone else's immoral act. Also, rare situations like these should not be used as justification for abortion on demand at any time and for any reason.

"The baby won't have a good life because they will be poor, disabled, etc."
Human value is not based on one's socio-economic status or health. Offering the baby for adoption is a godly alternative for families who believe they are incapable of raising a child at the time.

"Pro-lifers just want to control women's bodies."
The pro-life movement is not about controlling a woman's body. In fact, many people in the movement are women, and more than half of aborted babies are female. The primary objection to abortion is that the procedure kills a human being.

"It is inconsistent to be pro-life while being in favor of the death penalty."
This argument attempts to change the subject by introducing an irrelevant topic. Abortions end the life of the most innocent of lives while the death penalty is reserved for violent criminals.

ABOUT ABORTION

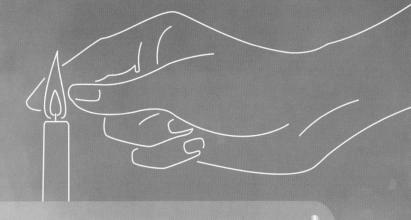

WHAT IS ABORTION?

In medical terminology, the termination of a pregnancy prior to delivery is called an abortion. Miscarriages are technically referred to as involuntary spontaneous abortions. When a woman voluntarily terminates her pregnancy, it is known as an induced abortion, and this is what is generally meant by the term *abortion*.

On January 22, 1973, the Supreme Court of the United States rendered a 7-2 ruling in *Roe v. Wade* that essentially legalized abortion throughout the country by striking down state and federal regulations against the procedure. As of January 2020, an estimated 60 million legal abortions have been performed in the United States. This is more than the population of California and New York combined.

WORLDVIEW IMPACT ON THE UNBORN

A person's position on origins and reality shapes how they view human life.

NATURALISTIC EVOLUTIONARY WORLDVIEW

From a naturalistic evolutionary perspective, morality is arbitrary and human beings have no more inherent value than an animal, a blade of grass, a rock, or anything else. Thus, ending human life via abortion or euthanasia carries no moral implications and is consistent with the evolutionary philosophy built on death and suffering.

BIBLICAL WORLDVIEW

Since the Bible states that all people are made in the image of God, all human life from fertilization until death has unlimited value. Thus, the termination of human life through abortion and euthanasia are antithetical to the biblical worldview.

ADOPTION
A GODLY ALTERNATIVE

Many pregnant women fear that they will be unable to properly care for their child once he or she is born. At the same time, countless couples struggle to have children, and others who already have children long to adopt and raise that child in a loving home.

In each of these situations, adoption is a godly alternative to abortion. Adoption allows a mother to give her baby an opportunity to live while also blessing a family with a child they have longed for.

Romans 8:15 teaches that believers are adopted into God's family. Like a loving father who cares for someone else's child as his own, God loves and nurtures those He has adopted into His family—those who have received His forgiveness through faith in the Lord Jesus Christ.

James 1:27 states that pure religion consists of caring for widows and orphans. A great way that Christians can live out this verse is to adopt children and raise them to love the Lord.

STORIES OF BELONGING

My husband and I were heartbroken when we discovered we would not be able to have biological children. But God turned our mourning into joy when He opened the door for us to adopt a beautiful baby girl from China. Our daughter has brought us laughter, adventure, and the privilege of seeing a young person love God and live for Him. We also have the distinct privilege of living out an earthly example of a profound spiritual truth: God's adoption of us as His children when we receive Christ as our Savior.

Georgia

I was adopted by a Christian family, even though they had only seen pictures of me and already had children. My new family loved and accepted me. They taught me the truth of Scripture and shared the gospel. Eventually, I surrendered my life to Christ.

Through adoption, I realized, "I'm chosen." As an adult, I visited my biological family, and I came to understand that God ordained my adoption. He protected and provided for me through my adoptive family.

Frances

WHAT HAPPENS
TO A BABY WHO DIES?

Since the Bible does not directly answer this question, many Christians have attempted to answer it by appealing to God's good and perfect character and by considering the following passages, which they believe are relevant to the topic.

The children sacrificed to pagan gods are described as innocent.
(Psalm 106:37-38; Jeremiah 19:4-5)

Jesus instructed His disciples to let little children come to Him and before blessing the children, He said, "to such belongs the kingdom of heaven." (Mark 10:15-16)

David confidently expressed that he would see his deceased child again.
(2 Samuel 12:23)

All of those sentenced to the lake of fire are judged according to their own works (Revelation 20:13), so it does not seem as if unborn babies will be part of this judgment.

Taken together, these ideas are used to support the idea that babies who die in the womb will be with the Lord eternally. Many Christians believe this notion extends to children and those with certain mental disabilities preventing them from comprehending the consequences of their actions and their need for the Savior. However, not all Christians agree with the above reasoning and caution against drawing firm conclusions on this issue.

While the Bible may not provide a direct answer to this question, all Christians can agree with Abraham's belief that **our Creator, the Judge of all the earth will do what is right** (Genesis 18:25).

——— STORIES OF **HOPE** ———

We excitedly announced our pregnancy when we were about seven weeks along. But at our ten-week appointment we were deeply saddened to find out we lost our baby. We still have moments of great sadness, grieving what could have been.
We are thankful for how the church loved and rallied around us. God is good and is the God of all comfort, and we've learned to count it all joy knowing that what seems hard He will redeem for good.

Paige

My husband and I endured three miscarriages in about a year, and it's been difficult to express my tremendous sense of loss. Even my husband said that it took a while for him to understand the depth of my grief, but he has been extremely supportive ever since. One of our greatest comforts came from having a biblical worldview. Knowing that all death and sorrow was a result of Adam's sin rather than being part of God's original creation helped me work through our emotions with hope, trust, and even joy. Indeed, Jesus Christ is our living hope!

Heather

CAN GOD STILL LOVE ME?

This question has been asked countless times by people who have struggled to come to grips with their past.

The truth is that all have sinned and fallen short of the glory of God (Romans 3:23). Humans have rebelled against our perfectly holy God in every way imaginable—lying, theft, rape, murder, etc., and we deserve to be judged for our sins.

Other than Jesus, our biblical heroes were flawed individuals. Jacob deceived people, Rahab lived as a prostitute, and Peter denied Jesus three times. Moses, David, and Paul wrote large sections of the Bible, yet they either murdered people or condemned innocent people to death. **But all these people found God's love, grace, and forgiveness.**

It is difficult to understand why God would be willing to forgive people who have done terrible things. However, this notion overlooks the fact that every sin is a crime against our Creator, and it fails to account for His amazing love for humanity.

God loves His creation, and He has provided the means for us to be forgiven. Jesus Christ, the Son of God, died in our place on the cross, paying the penalty for our sins. Then He demonstrated His power over death when He rose from the grave. Forgiveness of sins and eternal life are promised to "whoever believes in him" (John 3:15–18, Acts 10:43).

STORIES OF FORGIVENESS

I reasoned that my only option was abortion. No one informed me how incredibly dark that abortion experience would be, and how it would literally eat away at my soul. God finally stopped my downward spiral of self-destruction and showed me that He wanted me to have a close personal relationship with Him. Through a Bible study written by someone who had had an abortion, someone who had been in my shoes, I found the answers I had been searching for my whole life. I had a fresh desire to know the God who created me and had a plan for my life.

Camille

I never wanted children. I made up my mind. I drove Sandy to an abortion clinic and dropped her off. That day, a part of us died. Later, she confessed waiting for me to burst through the door of that abortion clinic and save her and my baby, but I didn't. I was a coward. I feared man, but not God. God began to work on my heart. Once I grasped the depth of my sin, looking at what Christ had done on the Cross, it came into full view in my mind that my sin had been fully dealt with and I could fully live in repentance and faith. God did a thorough work in my heart, my life, and my marriage.

Chad

231

The Ark Encounter is a one-of-a-kind, historically-themed attraction that features a full size, all wood Ark.

Located in Williamstown, Kentucky, the Ark Encounter is the largest timber-frame structure in the USA, with three levels and over 130 exhibit bays within the ship. The experience points to the feasibility of Noah's Ark and the authority of God's Word.

978-0-89051-507-5

NOAH'S ARK: THINKING OUTSIDE THE BOX

by TIM LOVETT

FIGURING OUT THE DESIGN

Genesis might be an abbreviated version of God's instructions about the ark, or perhaps Noah was smart enough to fill in the details himself. In either case, we are encouraged to investigate (Prov. 25:2 "It is the glory of God to conceal a matter; to search out a matter is the glory of kings."). There are three places to look — the Bible, testable science, and tradition.

The Bible: The reliable, yet sometimes brief, record of Noah's ark.

Testable Science: Engineering principles might help to fill in more detail and hopefully bring us closer to God's complete specifications (or Noah's ingenuity). Designing a ship requires a balance of many factors. Some are essential (like staying afloat), while others are only preferable (like ease of construction).

Essential factors: Won't leak, break, or capsize. Ride is not dangerously rough. Can be built with available technology. Houses all the animals and food safely.

Preferable factors: Optimized for a comfortable ride and best living conditions. Ease of construction. Low maintenance during voyage.

Another form of testable science is an artifact, but nothing has been found of Noah's ark. However, we do have artifacts from ancient ships that match historical records. These might hold clues since Noah's ark was the first ship in our (post-flood) history.

Tradition: Clues might be gleaned from Flood legends and ancient technologies.

True operational science should not conflict with the Bible. Unfortunately, even operational science can make mistakes, in which case the Bible overrules. Likewise, it would be wise to let operational science overrule legends.

Clearly the challenges Noah faced were daunting. Little is known of Noah or of the engineering abilities, tools, or craftsmanship of people of the time.

Make yourself an ark of gopherwood; make rooms in the ark, and cover it inside and outside with pitch. And this is how you shall make it: The length of the ark shall be three hundred cubits, its width fifty cubits, and its height thirty cubits. You shall make a window for the ark, and you shall finish it to a cubit from above; and set the door of the ark in its side. You shall make it with lower, second, and third decks. (Gen. 6:14–16).

Master Books®
A Division of New Leaf Publishing Group
www.masterbooks.com

Faithful to the biblical dimensions, Lovett reveals a feasible ark design, explores the impact of Flood waters on the vessel, and provides remarkable insight into the skills and techniques needed to construct it.

Here one can see the progress being made as the Amish team puts together more bents. The first one took two weeks to assemble and raise into place. They were eventually able to do two in a week's time.

The Ark construction with six bents fully in place.

Now with 15 bents in place, and starting on the outer skin as well.

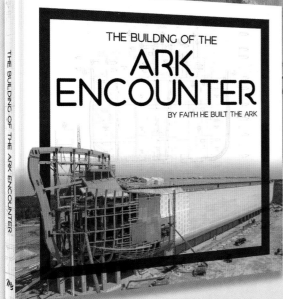

THE BUILDING OF THE ARK ENCOUNTER
BY FAITH HE BUILT THE ARK

Discover details of this engineering masterpiece as the largest timber-framed building in the world. At 510 feet long, 85 feet wide, and 51 feet high based on the Bible's dimensions, it presents the world with an awe-inspiring reminder of the scriptural account of the Ark.

978-0-89051-931-8

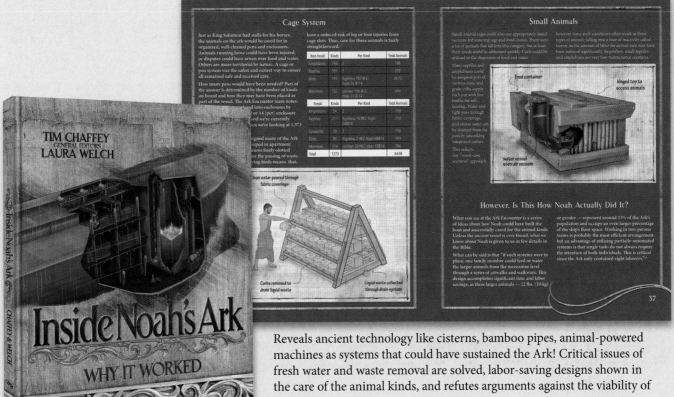

TIM CHAFFEY
LAURA WELCH
GENERAL EDITORS

Inside Noah's Ark
WHY IT WORKED

Reveals ancient technology like cisterns, bamboo pipes, animal-powered machines as systems that could have sustained the Ark! Critical issues of fresh water and waste removal are solved, labor-saving designs shown in the care of the animal kinds, and refutes arguments against the viability of the Ark!

978-0-89051-932-5

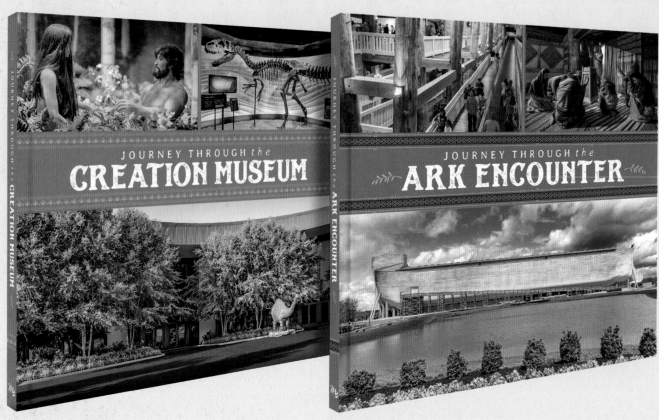

978-1-68344-147-2

978-1-68344-012-3

Relive the awe-inspiring experience of touring the Creation Museum. Filled with beautiful photography capturing dozens of spectacular exhibits and vibrant gardens, this book will surely be read time and time again.
For those who have never visited this world-class facility dedicated to upholding the authority of Scripture from the very first verse, you can now enjoy the next-best-thing to a visit and see why millions of people consider the Creation Museum a must-see destination.

Take an amazing tour through the pages of this book as the world's true history is shared through unique, world-class exhibits. Experience the reality of Noah's Ark, an immense wooden ship built to biblical dimensions to survive the violent forces of the global Flood. See common-sense solutions that would have enabled eight people to care for the animals. Discover the Ark's remarkable animal kinds, based on a multi-year study of both living and extinct creatures.

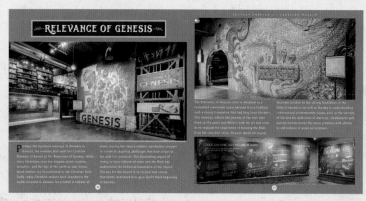